Eat, Drink and Be Wary

BY F. J. SCHLINK

CO-AUTHOR OF "100,000,000 GUINEA PIGS"

Covici · Friede · Publishers

NEW YORK

MANUFACTURED IN THE UNITED STATES OF AMERICA
BY J. J. LITTLE AND IVES COMPANY, NEW YORK

THIS BOOK is dedicated to those fortunate 13,000,000 Guinea Pigs more or less of America's population whose income permits them to eat what they need,[1] and whose aid is bespoken to get both quantity and quality of food for those who are hungry in the midst of Planned Starvation.

[1] Only about ten per cent of the population receive an income which permits them to eat good, well selected foods in adequate amounts, according to official statements of the U. S. Department of Agriculture functionaries (who are among the fortunate ten per cent) in hearings on the agricultural appropriation bill held March 25, 1935. See pages 3, 11 and 12 of the official record of the hearings.

CONTENTS

Contents

FOREWORD

This is a first, preliminary book in a field of very great importance to every person living in civilization. The amount of material available in the files of Consumers' Research on subjects within the scope of this book is so great that it would take a staff of three or four research workers two years or more to put it into form for publication. Topics of the greatest importance have had to be omitted entirely from the present work. For example, a sizable book could be written on the sanitary and chemical horrors of the ice cream, bottled soda, and soda fountain trades. Another is needed on the modern development of the drug store lunch-counter and commercial restaurants; the latter are fast degenerating into places where cans and bottles are opened, their contents heated and served, and the "empties" piled high in the alley. A long chapter must yet be written on the fake and distorted scientific research favoring factory-processed foods that has been furthered by the canners and their trade organizations and affiliates; another on the dangerous attacks on public health made by the sugar and candy manufacturers through their exploitative, misleading propaganda, the basis of which has often been purchased from physicians and scientists in much the same way that consumers buy butter at the corner store.

There will be many who will question the right of the author of this book to speak in the field of food and nutrition. Perhaps, when they have read Chapters I, II, XI, and XII, they may be less inclined to raise questions on this

score. There are many who are better qualified than the
author to write this work, but for one reason or another,
as it was necessary to point out also in the foreword of
100,000,000 Guinea Pigs, this job has been left to persons
working with Consumers' Research. So long as the official nutrition scientists are content to see the American
dietary continually debased for the great milling and baking
monopolies, and to salve their consciences with the recommendation of "protective foods," green leafy vegetables, and
milk, for a population which is less and less able to afford
the cheapest and most necessary staple foods, it will be necessary for outsiders and upstarts, if you please, like the
present author to help point the way to proper nutrition.
Those who will read Chapter I of this book will find what
McCollum, Sherman, and Mendel, those great doctors of
nutritional science, prefer to work at—instead of furnishing
for a helpless and exploited public the very necessary and
useful kinds of information which this book seeks to bring
together.

There is an honest, scientific middle ground between the
green leafy vegetables "protective foods" cult of McCollum
and Sherman, and the quack food advisers who scorn cooked
or flesh foods, or spread persuasive propaganda for spinach,
bran, buttermilk, acidophilus milk, or raw carrots.

This book will show that for most people the best advice
will be to return, so far as a complex industrial civilization
permits, to a simple traditional dietary, using as little as
possible of advertised, commercially manufactured, refined,
processed, artificially-ripened and treated foods, and consuming as much as possible of foods which are the least
removed in time and space from their original condition,
flavor, freshness, and natural environment. Such a return to

simplicity and directness of production and consumption of foods would represent a complete reversal of a dominant trend in our civilization—the trend toward interfering with Nature for a profit, at every possible point where a profit can be taken and a "service" charged for. One should remember that there are many other things about Nature besides its food supply which are extremely unlikely to be significantly improved by the intervention of the chemists, the production engineers, and the canned goods brokers.

The instinct which guides the cat and the robin to a proper selection of food for health and healthful activity, will work for man, and has worked for some hundreds of thousands of years for many races in many climes. If that be granted, it is clear that there is no reason whatever why the factory owner and the advertiser should be permitted to dictate to human beings on any subject so delicate and so important, individually and racially, as the determination of one's choice of food and its quality, purity, and freedom from adulteration. Let your mind and your instincts (and in civilization, you will need both) determine your diet: let others follow the billboards and *The Saturday Evening Post*.

I

THE MISINFORMERS — BUSINESS AND THE HIRE SCIENCE OF FOOD

This is a book about eating. There are few who question the importance of eating, but the number who know what to eat for good health and well-being are, among Americans, almost a vanishing race, due largely to the false light shed over the dinner table by the "scientific nutritionists," the professional dietitians, the home-economists, the vitamin zealots, the raw food cultists, the Battle Creek nut, cereal, bran, and meat-substitute fanciers, the white bread enthusiasts, the gentry of the opposite, or cattle-food camp, who favor the eating of bran, and even the diet-and-shape experts from Hollywood. Perhaps the decision to write this book grew, as much as from any single factor, out of the recent discovery that Margaret Sullavan, a girl certainly with excellent hips but no noticeable or submitted knowledge of the correct basis of eating, came out boldly for bread on behalf of General Mills, Inc. Co-stars in Miss Sullavan's testimonials for bread, rolls, and toast, were Claudette Colbert, Sylvia Sidney, Oscar of the Waldorf, Lafayette B. Mendel, Ph. D., Sc. D., E. V. McCollum, Ph. D., Sc. D., Raymond Hertwig of the American Medical Association, and Emily Post. Mrs. Post contributes the truly remarkable idea that "breads—an increasing number of breads—are the indispensable items of every provision made by a hostess" and that "at a perfectly appointed formal dinner . . . three breads are the minimum: finger rolls, melba toast and rye brittle bread. . . . The one inflexible rule of etiquette concerning the afternoon tea menu, is that *nothing* unassociated with the product of a bakery is suitable. . . . Unless the sweets or sours, the roes or the patés, the meat or fish or salad is put on top of, or between bread of one sort or another, it is tabu according to the best conventions of social usage." A most convenient etiquette for the bread industry.

Drs. McCollum and Mendel followed the high standard of intellectual content established by the etiquette expert, and provide in the booklet, *Vitality Demands Energy—109 Smart New Ways to serve BREAD Our Outstanding Energy Food,* a line of argument that could have been applied with almost equal precision to cornstarch pudding or peanut brittle. The gist of the reasoning of these great doctors of food science and of the American Medical Association's endorser of the bleached-white-flour trade, Raymond Hertwig, is that baker's bread is a fine food if you don't depend on it for much of anything but energy, i.e., Calories—which is a slightly qualified way of saying (but this would be clear only to another expert) that you shouldn't depend on it!

Dr. McCollum's statements and quotations of opinions attributed to him have by their dangerous inconsistency and in other ways contributed so extensively to the misinformation of the common man and the miseducation of young people taking courses in nutrition and home-economics that even among eminent teachers of nutrition Dr. McCollum takes a stellar place. He is quoted, for example, by the American Housewife's Bureau, an organization which, despite its name, is a publicity agency for canned foods, as approving on the basis of nutritional research "the high favor of canned foods among consumers." But on page

18 of this book the reader can determine for himself that Dr. McCollum considers the growing dependence upon grocery store items, including canned goods, as a "new and hitherto untried experiment in human nutrition." The layman will understand the flexibility of thought among some who qualify as scientists which permits the same man to say of canned goods at one time that their high favor among consumers is justified by the results of nutritional research, and at another time that American dependence upon them constitutes a part of a "new and hitherto untried experiment in human nutrition."

It is important to note that (according to the advertising of General Mills, Inc., in the *Journal of Home Economics*) everything said by Mr. Hertwig is specifically approved by Professors Mendel and McCollum. Among the points made by Hertwig in his "Bleached White Flour Wholesome" written for General Mills, Inc., is that "white flour is a wholesome food and has a proper place in the well balanced, adequate diet"; also that "it is good nutrition to include a goodly proportion of white flour products in the diet if sufficient of [certain] other foods . . . are also used."

In hearings on an agricultural appropriation bill in March, 1935, Dr. McCollum wrote to the Senator in charge, signing himself with his full title and university connection, so there can be no question of his having taken responsibility both directly and indirectly for favoring white-flour bread: "The writer [McCollum] . . . has written extensively for popular reading, with a view to combating the pernicious teachings of food faddists who have sought to make people afraid of white-flour bread."

But in 1928 in *Food, Nutrition and Health* by Dr. McCollum and Dr. Nina Simmonds, these authors said: "The

American public has been educated to like white bread and
white flour. This liking has been created by skillful advertising. Whiteness suggests purity and the more expensive
flours being the whitest have come to be regarded as the most
desirable, but the appetite and instinct of man do not necessarily guide him aright in the selection of his foods. There
is no logical basis for the selection of a spongy, white bread
instead of a coarse dark bread. The former does not have
to be chewed much, the latter demands exercise to reduce
it to a condition suitable for swallowing. Poor people, especially in foreign countries, have eaten coarse black breads
and so these came to be looked down upon by the aristoc-
racy. The poor Chinaman whose arduous toil yields but a
few cents a day often buys polished rice rather than un-
polished to satisfy his vanity, and suffers from a deficiency
disease—beri-beri—as a result, whereas if he had eaten
whole rice he would have escaped this misfortune. Pride is at
the bottom of a number of common and serious errors in
the selection of food."

It is a curious fact that in the 1933 edition of this book,
on which Dr. Simmonds' name does not appear, her place
being taken by J. Ernestine Becker, one does not find this
significant and forthright paragraph. Dr. McCullum's
writings however do not appear to produce a single line of
evidence that would justify his having retreated from his
1928 position, unfavorable to white flour, to his 1934 position, in which he is associated with Mendel and Hertwig in
a justification of baker's bread made of bleached white flour.
Nor does competent evidence to justify such a shift exist.
(Indeed the need for dark bread was far greater in 1934
than in 1928.) McCullum's shift is clearly against the evidence, and clearly in the direction of the incessant commer-

cial pressure that General Mills, Inc., and their ad-men have
applied to home-economics and nutrition workers in the
schools, colleges, and universities everywhere.

In his larger book, *The Newer Knowledge of Nutrition*
(1929), McCollum is even more positive against white bread
than in his 1928 publication: "In point of quantity consumed white flour is the most important energy food in
America and Europe. This is important because it is notably deficient in more dietary factors than any other food
entering into the diet, except sugars, starches and fats
which are sold in the pure state. It consists essentially of
starch, proteins and inorganic salts. Its proteins are of relatively poor quality and its mineral components are poor in
calcium, sodium, chlorine, iron, and phosphorus. . . .
Wheat flour is very deficient in all vitamins."

As though to condemn the way in which General Mills
uses the pronouncements of nutrition experts, including
himself, to justify the use of white flour, McCollum, on page
115 of the same book, says: "The polishing of rice is done
to improve its keeping quality, and the incidental whitening
of the kernels led to a demand for a white product. *This,
and the artificially established liking for white flour and
white corn meal, is an illustration of the failure of the instinct of man to serve as a safe guide in the selection of
food.* The esthetic sense is appealed to in greatest measure
in this case by the products of lowest biologic values." It
would be hard to provide a more convincing disproof of the
statements which McCollum made and supported in the
General Mills pamphlet, *Vitality*. It seems entirely fair to
say that, if, in McCollum's own italicized phrase, the instinct of man fails "to serve as a safe guide in the selection
of food," the intelligence of man, if counseled by the great

doctors of nutrition, from Johns Hopkins and Yale, is an even less safe guide, and that either instinct or the testimonials of nutrition experts serve alike to lead the race to "products of lowest biologic values." What a responsibility, when men's instincts are not to be trusted, to confound them by untrustworthy advice!

When Dr. McCollum said, in his statement for the *Vitality* booklet, "The statements which follow are merely the high points brought out in my popular book, *Food, Nutrition and Health*, and therefore, represent the ideas which I have emphasized for many years in my lectures and writings. . . . Bread, in my opinion, should form the principal source of energy in the American diet," he is in effect but saying that the readers of General Mills' advertising will not *read* what he actually "emphasized for many years in . . . [his] writings." He will be right; it is a familiar technique of advertising men to push the sales of dental and medical nostrums by closing with the advice: "Ask your dentist," or "Ask your doctor"; in doing so they know that the suggested verification of the advertisement will not be carried out by more than a trifling percentage of readers. But no one who would take the time to read McCollum's writings carefully could be in the least misled by General Mills' advertising—or even by McCollum's contribution to it.

In another place in *Food, Nutrition and Health*, McCollum again emphasizes the hazardous nature of the eating of white flour, referring to its use in combination with sugar and canned, dried, and cold storage foods, as a "hitherto untried experiment in human nutrition." Is such mass-experimentation with the health of young and old, rich and poor, one of those things a nutrition scientist can justify, for General Mills, Inc.?

Food Field Reporter of March 26, 1934, a very business-like trade journal, nicely sums up the adjustability of nutrition experts' functioning:

"Professor E. V. McCollum of Baltimore and Professor Lafayette B. Mendel of New Haven will urge scientific *arguments in favor of* eating bread. [Italics mine.]

"On March 24 the campaign went on the air with an all-star feature program, utilizing orchestras, stage and screen stars, dramatizations, and comedy, with the professors at the microphone as well. The Betty Crocker broadcasts will be devoted exclusively to uses of bread, beginning March 21."

Perhaps this crass juxtaposition of nutrition science, "arguments-in-favor" and Betty Crocker broadcasts—with dramatizations—may enable McCollum's readers to know how much weight they shall give to his recently expressed judgment favorable to the use of vitamin D in foods. Referring to "wide publicity [given] to the poisonous character of large doses of vitamin D" and to many people's becoming "apprehensive of the danger of eating foods vitaminized by the addition of activated ergosterol," McCollum says, "this . . . is a false alarm." Perhaps no more a false alarm in terms of what an eminent nutritionist may express at some other time and place and for a commercial client, than were Dr. McCollum's own 1928 and 1929 views on the highly experimental nature of the general consumption of white flour and white bread made therefrom.

Again though opposed to white bread in *Food, Nutrition and Health*, Dr. McCollum, in an article called "What Is a Sensible Attitude Toward Food?" is for it, and this time discloses the business bias of nutrition science. "There are good and sound commercial reasons why most people should eat white bread. . . . It is safest and most economical to transport the refined flour and to get it to the consumer in the form of bread than [sic] it is if whole wheat flour were used, since the latter tends to spoil more readily."

It is not necessary to give so much space to the contradictions of opinion of Nutrition-Scientist Mendel, who has perhaps been less distinguished for this type of propaganda activity than McCollum, but it is sufficient to refer the reader to page 69 in Chapter IV where Mendel is shown to have expressed in 1927 and 1932 a critical judgment in respect to the very process and type of food best illustrated by the modern, highly milled bleached white flour for which he now performs in an advertiser's rôle. It is hardly necessary to state that in his endorsement of white flour for General Mills, Mendel does not refer in the disparaging terms he used in his American Medical Association *Journal* article to the "numerous highly milled cereal products and other cereal novelties," nor to his own statement that "Rice, in the process of polishing, has lost most of its vitamins, and the same is true of other highly milled cereals." The *chief* of the "other highly milled cereals" is of course the bleached white flour of General Mills, Inc., and other leading millers.

An advertising journal with a frankness and honesty almost unique in the publications of the profession, in a report on a session of a professional society, at which scientists discussed nutritional qualities of bread, gives the truth of this controversy of McCollum versus McCollum and Mendel versus Mendel in this succinct form: "White and part-rye brands showed about one-third and one-half, respectively, the [vitamin B] value of whole wheat bread.

"The American public demands white bread and thus the milling industry is obliged to continue the practice of dis-

carding from cereals their outer layers which contain the
valuable minerals and vitamins naturally present in the
whole grain. Ironically, these by-products are utilized in
cattle and poultry feeds to provide these same essential
nutritive factors. It is significant that approximately one-
third of the caloric intake of the American diet comes from
cereals stripped of their minerals and vitamins. These should
be restored to bread or the term 'staff of life' becomes a
misnomer. . . .

"Again white bread was vastly inferior to whole wheat
bread in causing hemoglobin regeneration [replacement of
the red pigment of the blood], owing to a higher iron and
copper content in the whole wheat bread."

General Mills' expensive booklet—which glorifies the great
American wheat-spoiling industry that mills chemically
bleached white flour and sells it mainly to bakers who chemi-
calize it still more with yeast foods, chemical flavor rein-
forcers, butter substitutes, nut substitutes, egg substitutes,
milk substitutes, and even, incredible as it may seem, yeast
substitutes and flour substitutes—ends on an appropriate
note. It is bread, it seems, that gives the Hollywood stars
their vitality. The peculiar movie-actress smirk in the pictures of this beautifully printed booklet of General Mills
probably has nothing to do with bread, but represents the
influence of advertising upon the countenances of women
made "vital" with bread and blessed by association with
those great doctors of nutrition, McCollum (Johns Hopkins) and Mendel (Yale). It is interesting that both of the
learned doctors found it inexpedient to permit mention in
the advertising of the names of their universities. University
science has stood for much, but it has been providentially
spared, in this instance, association with the great art repre-

sented by Will Hays, the antique-castle-collector William Randolph Hearst, the Warner Brothers, Ann Dvorak, Bette Davis, and Mary Astor. The three last named get their words and pictures in the booklet, where their opinions about the essential nature of baker's bread reinforce those of the learned savants, McCollum, Mendel, and Hertwig. The modern advertising agency expert, please note, catches his customers with whatever types of bait seem to work!

To the writer of this book it seems that when the American regard for advice from high-placed persons goes to the point of hearkening to a movie actress—at one end of the scale of scholarship, salary, and pulchritude—and assorted college professors and nutrition experts far too much concerned with "good and sound commercial reasons [favoring the use of] white bread"—at the other end of the scale—it is time someone raised a voice in protest at such culinary indignities, and in defense of the American stomach.

There are many millions, probably nine-tenths of the population of the United States according to official statements of the U. S. Department of Agriculture, who in these New Deal days are quite unable to get enough to eat of first-class food, and nearly as many who do not get enough, even as to quantity, of essential foods, such as meat, fish, poultry, eggs, butter, fresh fruit, and fresh vegetables of high nutritional quality. The other tenth (accepting the estimate made by the Department of Agriculture's representatives [1]) find their fare in stale, boxed, dried, canned, bottled, pickled, over-sugared, bleached, and refined food

[1] Given in the hearings on the agricultural appropriation bill held March 25, 1935; see pages 3, 11, and 12 of the official record of the hearings.

supplies, and eat great quantities of chocolate bars, ice cream, and baker's cakes, and canned peaches, pears, plums, and cherries, and other sweets masquerading as foods, consuming endless quantities of soda pop, *Coca-Cola*, *Whistle*, *Orange-Kist*, and *Moxie*, and travel from restaurant to home to dining car with only occasional and often accidental lapses into the sort of diet upon which their forebears throve and lived to a hearty old age without benefit of surgery and sanatoria and of General Foods and General Mills.

II

MISINFORMATION AT WHOLESALE
—THE WOMEN'S HOME MAGAZINES

Hearst's *Good Housekeeping* May Be Very Bad
Housekeeping

Let us look for a moment upon the pages of those journals of dim light and misleading from which the average middle-class, comfortably housed, and vaguely ailing homemaker gets her ideas about the science of the kitchen and the table.

Mr. Hearst's *Good Housekeeping* is the most widely read of the group, and the one most believed. Does it not have a *Good Housekeeping Institute* which *guarantees* (see page 6 of each issue) everything that is advertised, and inferentially everything that is said editorially? Unfortunately the guidance of the home magazines all too often misguides the home-economist and dietitian who, exactly as the layman, are unaware of the extent to which experts get their inspiration and even the detailed organization of their findings, experiments, and tests, from the subsidies made by Big Business to Big Education and to Science—which is appropriately spelled with a capital letter and more and more often directed and influenced exactly as though it were spelled $cience.

In *Good Housekeeping* in two recent issues, we find the following instances of "guidance" for the literate and prosperous housewife, and for the high school and college teacher of home-economics.

"The [breakfast] cereal habit is excellent, especially because cereals are usually eaten with milk or cream."

The truth: The national breakfast cereal habit is *not* excellent. It is the undesirable result of high-pressure and misleading advertising, concentrated in this field because large-scale, misleading advertising made it possible to reap very large profits on very simple and cheap raw materials and processes, crisped and puffed and shredded and flaked to handsome prices—per pound and per breakfast.

Says *Good Housekeeping:* [There were] "Cereals with extra germ added to provide the rather scarce vitamin B, which stimulates appetite and aids in preventing nervousness and fatigue."

What does that say for the far commoner, widely advertised cereals, such as Cream-of-Wheat, which lack essential mineral constituents of the whole wheat and from which the germ with its valuable protein, fat, and vitamin has been removed? How can Miss Elizabeth Frazer (who writes the article in *Good Housekeeping* magazine from which these two items are quoted) have it both ways, except that her readers do not know that the desirable way to make a cereal food is to leave the grain alone so far as possible, not adding vitamin B—*nor* subtracting it from *Kracksy Krackles* to add it (for a fee) to *Krumply Krumbles?*

Further in this nutritionally misleading article, the readers of *Good Housekeeping* are told that the idea of packaging breakfast foods came into being because an oatmeal miller saw some of his product treated in unsanitary fashion in a grocer's store.

The packaging technique *in fact* grew up because there is

much more money to be made in selling by the package than
by the pound. People who buy by the pound have an unpleasant way of shopping for the lowest price, precisely as food
manufacturers do in their purchase of raw materials and
supplies. People who can be persuaded to buy by the package have a habit of not noting, or of forgetting what their
foods come to, per pound, or per breakfast.

Byron MacFadyen, who is head of the food advertising
department of an advertising agency and bears the title of
"liaison officer" of N. W. Ayer & Son, writes a series of
articles for *Good Housekeeping* which the innocent reader
supposes is just good, homey advice about food cookery.
But MacFadyen manages to work in constant hints helpful
to the food processing and advertising businesses—perhaps
to his own advertising business in particular—urging his
readers to use canned mushrooms, ready-grated Parmesan or
American cheese, canned consommé, bouillon cubes, canned
tomato paste, jelly, etc. And so direct a hint as "In menus
where spaghetti takes the place of potatoes the canned
variety is most appropriate. It's a great convenience to be
able to have this fragrant dish at a moment's notice by
merely heating the contents of the can. And the chefs who
prepare these popular brands have demonstrated that they
know the secret of blending tomatoes, condiments, cheese,
and spaghetti into an appetizing, colorful assembly."

Point 1: Spaghetti shouldn't, and from a nutritional
standpoint, can't, take the place of potatoes. Point 2: The
canned variety, especially, of spaghetti can never be "appropriate" as a substitute for fresh cooked or baked potatoes
or any other good fresh food. The difference between out-
and-out advertising and writing "articles" which readers
are supposed to accept as uninfluenced by commercial in-

terest is thus, one sees, a trifling dissimilarity—except that
the *articles* are more insidious and more likely to be believed, because the services of Mr. MacFadyen and Miss
Frazer to advertising are not known and are not made
known to the readers.

Another of Mr. MacFadyen's articles devotes itself in
quite irrational but profit-making fashion to the puffing of
factory-made grocery store relishes, such as pickles, chow-
chow, India relish, mustard sauce, chili sauce, catsup,
Worcestershire, horse-radish, store jelly, and that old reliable profit-maker, factory-made mayonnaise. "You'll find it
profitable to stock up [at the store] with a selection of these
zestful creations." And for a going-to-bed dish, MacFadyen
suggests scrambled eggs with chili sauce. What gin- and
canned-goods jaded appetites *Good Housekeeping's* readers must be assumed to have, to need chili sauce in their bed-
time scrambled eggs! For those to whom chili sauce is too
mild or uncomplicated, Mr. MacFadyen provides a recipe
"TESTED BY GOOD HOUSEKEEPING INSTITUTE" for using
Worcestershire sauce, cream, and paprika with fried eggs.

On one of Mr. MacFadyen's pages of awful cookery is
printed in a "box" an invitation to home-economics teachers
to write in for a "classified index," now ready, of Institute
articles and *teaching suggestions* based on these articles. It
is unfortunately true that thousands of home-economics
teachers will regard this material as entirely suitable for
classroom use and as unbiased and authoritative, rather
than business-motivated. If the teacher in your school is
using this kind of material and journals like *Good Housekeeping* and other women's magazines as a basis of teaching,
you may be sure that the education and information of your
children are being rapidly and effectively corrupted so far

as concerns their knowledge of and ability to choose and to prepare wholesome and nutritious foods.

"With such tables," [a very inadequate one of iron and copper content of common foods is given] says Dr. Walter Eddy, a professor in the home-economics school at Columbia University, also serving as an employe of *Good Housekeeping Institute,* "you can determine what foods will give you your necessary iron and copper."

You can do nothing of the sort, as Dr. Eddy admits in the very next paragraph on one good ground, viz., that iron and copper assimilation from foods depends upon a number of complex and little understood factors. But scientist Eddy fails to mention the other very important point: that copper is much *too* common in our average food supply, being regularly a contaminating substance in milk, cream, ice cream, canned foods, candy, and bakery goods, and in many other products that pass through food factory copper kettles and copper piping, or which have been at some stage sprayed by or exposed to copper-bearing insect sprays. (Bordeaux mixture, a copper-containing material, is one of the most used of the insect sprays.) Besides, copper is present in a very large part of our water supply, through treatment of water in reservoirs with copper salts, and through the increasing use of copper piping in street connections and in houses and offices.

"Vitamin A [is] important to cold resistance," says Dr. Eddy. But Dr. P. H. Long, in a paper before the Michigan Medical Society, shows that recent research nullifies this claim and quotes Dr. S. W. Clausen as suggesting even that too much vitamin A may predispose a child to infection of the respiratory tract! To quote from Dr. Long: "The failure of vitamin therapy as a prophylactic measure in colds

can be understood if one bears in mind that in general the
national dietary is not lacking in these essential substances.
. . . At present the only prophylaxis against colds is the
avoidance of contact with infected persons. There is no
other method." In other words, what Dr. Eddy says may not
be science, but merely something found convenient for the
readers of women's magazines to believe. After all, one can't
accept the view, as *Good Housekeeping's* Bureau of Foods,
Sanitation, and Health evidently does, that *Listerine* re-
lieves sore throat; that *Lux* toilet soap guards against cos-
METIC SKIN; and that *Vicks VapoRub* is the "*safe proved*
way to treat colds," and be too fussy about the interpretation of scientific findings.

Dr. Eddy, answering a reader's query, said in regard to enameled cooking ware: "Modern enamels do
not contain any toxic metal, so there is no poison to be released."

The truth: *Most* modern enamels were found according
to tests of Consumers' Research to contain *several* toxic
metals; on the basis of the limited work so far done, it
appears that very few indeed are even reasonably safe from
danger of solution of the poisonous metal compounds in acid
or alkaline foods cooked in an enamelware pan or kettle. It
might appear from Dr. Eddy's answer in this case that he
would not wish to report the truth. There is an ample literature of poisoning by enamelware, sometimes involving a large
number of people, and Consumers' Research, whose work is
widely known in Dr. Eddy's and *Good Housekeeping's* circles, has reported with brand names careful chemical analyses of the enamel linings of a number of widely sold brands
of American enamelware, nearly all of which were found
made of unsuitable materials.

Says Dr. Eddy: ". . . some one may have told you that gelatin is a good protein. It is. . . . It is not expensive."

Gelatin is *not* a good protein, and it is very expensive. Flavored gelatin, mostly used as a dessert, is hardly to be rated as more than an attractive way to dilute or "extend" sugar and artificial fruit flavor and color. Neither Dr. Eddy nor *Good Housekeeping* can ever, by any magic of words, turn factory-made gelatin into a valuable food or a "good protein."

Again, "Liberal use of milk makes the cereal proteins adequate and also makes possible a greater use of cereals as both protein and fuel supply." People whose means are sufficient to permit them the luxury of being misled by *Good Housekeeping's* food and nutrition articles do not *need* to use more cereals as protein and fuel supply. Use of cereals in considerable amounts is unfortunately necessary in the economy of Roosevelt and Wallace for those whose incomes cannot spare the amount required to buy *Good Housekeeping* each month. Those who can spend their money freely require no "liberal use of milk" except for feeding their young infants—and for that purpose the milk of cows is not preferred, however convenient or however necessary it may be in particular cases.

Dorothy B. Marsh of the "Institute Staff" writes that grown-ups and children over five years should have a "salad of lettuce, raw cabbage, carrot, etc., once a day. Cut the raw vegetable into strips. . . ." This is very bad advice. Some *grown* persons can eat raw vegetables occasionally. Few can or should eat them daily. There is no nutritional necessity for eating raw foods, *especially* raw vegetables. There is no scientific evidence of any such necessity—except for experimental animals such as guinea pigs, whose adaptation and habituation to raw foods is well known, and was well known indeed before the scientific nutritionists began their obscure and mainly irrelevant studies, on experimental animals. For children, unless in most robust health, the advice to eat raw vegetables, especially lettuce, cabbage, and carrots, is bad advice and as unwarranted as the general and unscientific prescribing of bran.

"Cod liver oil is beneficial to all," says the Institute Staff.

Cod liver oil is *not* beneficial to all. Cod liver oil is the very high price, and a risky one, paid for living in cities, wearing too many clothes, avoiding the sunlight, and eating artificial, preserved, stabilized, canned, ethylene-ripened, dyed, and over-processed foods too far removed, in growing and marketing, from sun and air and the realities of woodland, farm, and field. Under narrowly limited conditions, cod liver oil (advertised in *Good Housekeeping*) is *necessary* for some, but it is no more properly to be called beneficial than are epsom salts or castor oil. Like either of these, it may be necessary at times or even frequently, if the food supply is too much of the preserved, degerminated, devitaminized, oversweet or nutritionally imperfect kind recommended by *Good Housekeeping* and its leading advertisers—*Cocomalt, Mazola, Eagle Brand* Condensed Milk, *Midco Ice Box Freeze, Anglo* canned Corned Beef, *Armour's* canned Corn Beef Hash, *Liberty* bottled Cherries (maraschino), *Bireley's California Orangeade, Jelke's* oleomargarine, *Knox's* gelatine, *Royal Gelatine, Karo* corn syrup, canned deviled ham, *Pabst-ett* process cheese, *Swift's Premium Bacon, Kellogg's Rice Krispies*, factory ice cream, *Crisco, Royal Pud-*

dings, Certo for making jelly of far above normal sugar content, *Campbell's* soups, and long-lasting, Cellophane-wrapped, factory-made baker's goods.

Good Housekeeping furnishes something really unique in proposing, as its advertisements do, that one should get vitamin D from a complexion cream, Vita-Ray. Such an indirect way to derive vitamin D's values can only make sense in view of the kind of food supply which readers of *Good Housekeeping* will get by eating the foods which its advertisements and its reading matter recommend.

No housewife or home-economist should read the food articles in the women's magazines unless she has become very adept at detecting the trail of advertising interest in the editorials and the articles that pass for pure information. There is not space to discuss in this book the misleading character and content of most of the advertisements themselves, but this has been done often before in numerous bulletins of Consumers' Research, in *Your Money's Worth*, in *100,000,000 Guinea Pigs*, in *Skin Deep*, in various magazine articles, and especially in the November, 1934, and March, 1935, Bulletins of Consumers' Research in two interesting articles, where the technique used by Elizabeth Frazer of *Good Housekeeping* in articles about canned and package goods is given special examination. Read such magazines if you must, but don't feed your family on the foods or by the methods of cookery they recommend. They are in a very serious sense responsible for most of the things and most of the kinds of things that are wrong with the American dietary. The "literacy" of American housewives fed upon this kind of kitchen and pantry pabulum has left them much less well qualified to deal with the problem of their families' food supply—in fact—than the illiteracy of a Mexican or Indian or South Sea mother of a numerous brood of half-savage children who thrive on a diet at a small fraction of the American diet's cost, and without benefit of frequent consultation with a pediatrist! And where the women's magazines have failed completely to deliver the American housewife into the hands of General Mills and General Foods and Standard Brands, the home-economist has stepped energetically into the breach to give the right businesslike slant to the advice available to the oncoming generation. Our professional engineers worked themselves and the factory workmen out of jobs by improving the efficiency of the factory process, without deigning to concern themselves about the inefficiency of the economic process represented by bonds, mortgages, bank loans, preferred stock, stock dividends, enormous bonuses to steel and tobacco magnates, and the closing or bankruptcy in recent years of 60,000 small factories and the permanent unemployment of a large part of their workers. Our professional home-economists and home-economics teachers, in exactly the same way and in equal ignorance of the social meaning of their work, have helped mightily to turn farmers into operators of marginal, disappearing, uneconomic raw-material factories feeding great processing plants of Borden's, Kraft-Phenix, General Mills; and have turned the consumer at the other end of the farm-to-consumer chain into a food moron incapable any longer of recognizing the essential and deep-seated difference between the food value of "strawberry" gelatine and a cut of juicy, rare roast beef. "Gelatin," said Dr. Eddy, "is a good protein." Perhaps, then, Dr. Eddy, hoofs and hides, of which gelatin is made, are "good protein" too.

When you read *Good Housekeeping*, *The Ladies' Home Journal*, *The Delineator*, *McCall's*, and the *Woman's Home*

Companion, it is very necessary to remember that *articles* are written with an eye on the advertisements, or upon the advertiser who may yet be landed. It's advertisers' money that runs these journals; the readers exist solely to permit the magazines' corporate owners to tap advertisers as a source of income. It is not uncommon that ten times as much of the money that runs the journal comes from advertisers as from the readers who subscribe or buy the magazines on the newsstands. So when Elizabeth Fraser ends an imaginative and highly romantic and unscientific article on Fish, with the stereotype: "Yes, the fish are running! So let's go fishing—to the nearest grocery store!" she says grocery store rather than to the brook or the seaside or the fish market or fish wharf, because it is to *Good Housekeeping's* interests to send readers to the grocery store, where *manufactured* foods are sold, and profits are drained off to handsomely appointed executive offices in New York and Chicago. As the *Good Housekeeping* article makes all too plain, it is canned, trade-marked, *nationally advertised and advertisable* fish, mainly salmon and tuna, that are in mind all the while. (There are minor references to other trade-marked fish products, including canned fish cakes and quick-frozen fish fillets.) In one short article in an issue of *McCall's* magazine giving recipes for twelve dishes, eight of the items are based on a canned or preserved product; all of the items call for the use of advertised and packaged products. Illustrating perhaps the exceptionally close tie which exists between editorial and advertising departments in the household magazines, seven of the specific types of packaged food products mentioned in the text of the article are offered in advertisements in the same number of *McCall's.*

Here it may be in order to sum up briefly a few of the
leading and most harmful misconceptions that have been
put over on the American people by big business, from General Mills to the International Magazine Company (owner
of Hearst's *Good Housekeeping* and other popular journals
for the home), by big education, big advertising, and $cience
as it is known and operated on a sound business basis and
notably at such prominent and powerful institutions as Columbia University, the University of California, and Johns
Hopkins. Such beliefs are:

The well exploited idea that food in cans and bottles,
from canned chicken à la king to frankfurters bottled in
glass jars, is nearly or quite as good for one as savory
foods prepared fresh from fresh raw materials for the meal
at which they are eaten. For this delusion, the American
public has to thank the canners' association, the larger can
companies, the women's magazines, and the endless nonsense
of the newspapers' women's pages.

The belief that taste can be endlessly corrupted by sweets
and sweet beverages like ice cream and ice cream desserts and
sugared and chocolated drinks, and still remain a reliable
guide to one's nutritional life. The ice cream manufacturers,
the bottled drink manufacturers, and a dozen or so of college
professors and government officials have done their work
here.

The belief that elaborate disguises, color combinations,
and attractive contrasts of tint and texture in soups,
salads, cakes, meat dishes, and desserts, are an adequate substitute for fine food, well cooked and simply and honestly
served, without puffery or concealment of its essential character. This, the substitution of chromatics for dietetics, is

the field in which home-economists and all the women's home magazines have made the chief contribution to public ignorance and misleading.

The belief held peculiarly by American housewives of the middle and upper classes and even of the working class with strong climbing instincts, that the way to hold a man and keep him out of chop houses and night clubs where he might meet up with more interesting and more youthful females, is to wear lipstick of the "latest" shade, and to-mato-colored fingernail varnish, and feed him a cold canned-chicken and canned-pea salad platter with *G. Washington's* Instant Coffee or *Coca-Cola*—if only the platter be sufficiently garnished with water cress and parsley, and sliced canned pineapple with whipped cream and maraschino cherries. This shocking neglect of the age-old appeal of the fresh-roasted, farm-raised, not-cold-storage chicken prepared by a skilled and deft home-maker *sans* can opener, for the particular occasion and served at the exact moment when flavor and savor are right, is due to the women's magazines, and the newspapers' woman's pages, with valiant support from home-economics teachers.

The belief that study of methods of teaching at a normal school or teachers' college qualifies a young woman who cannot even bake a loaf of home-made bread to talk a whole generation out of its confidence in a safe, pure and unadulterated traditional diet on which its forebears have lived and kept well for many generations, and into a regime of *Puffed Wheat, Rice Krispies,* waffles, raw carrot and raisin salad, canned sweet potatoes with marshmallows, process-cheese, ice-box cake, cornstarch pudding, and graham cracker pie. This belief, of course, we owe to advertising and to the teachers in the teachers' colleges and normal schools and in the home-economics departments of state universities.

The belief that bran and other drastic, harsh roughage like spinach and raw lettuce can provide mechanical compensation in the intestinal tract for a sedentary or physically indolent life, a diet predominantly of sweets and starches, a habit of rising at eight and retiring at one or two a. m., an endless round of bridge, matinees and "spectator sports" and shopping for the newest in cocktail-glasses, clothes, and cosmetics. For this we must thank principally the women's magazines, the home-economists, and the business men who first discovered that a waste product of the white-flour milling trade could be turned into a great deal of money if put into a pretty package and advertised with a lavish hand.

The belief that dry and "durable" foods like crackers, process cheese and unripe cheese, crispy crackly corn flakes, pre-cooked oatmeal, rice, coffee, cocoa, canned salmon, canned grapefruit juice, canned baked apples drenched with sugar, canned peaches, plums and cherries of varieties especially chosen to endure the hardships of long journeys in trucks and long waits on the grocer's shelf, Crisco and other synthetic fats likewise noted for their durability, bottled bacon and frankfurters, canned soup, canned ham, catsup, pickles, store cakes and cookies, evaporated milk, ginger ale, near-jams and jellies low in their content of fruit and high in sugar and pectin, and anchovy paste, can take the place of a natural and traditional diet. A safe and proper diet should include each day, or frequently, generous quantities of fresh country eggs and fresh butter, fresh roasted and broiled meats, poultry and fish, savory stews, genuine and well-aged cheese, whole grain wheat and flour made from it, barley and whole rice, beans, carrots, peas, yellow squash in season and potatoes fresh from the garden or vegetable cellar, native fruits and nuts fresh from the orchard or the cellar or attic storage bin (*not* from the ethylene ripening process, or the sulphuring chamber or the lye or dye vat now held to be necessary to make attractive and uniform fruits and nuts for the table). For this misguidance we are mainly indebted to the women's home magazines, and their habitual allies, nutrition teachers and home-economics workers.

Even the drinking water of the urban middle classes is chlorinated, coppered, phenolized, and manganated, and otherwise contaminated with strange and poisonous chemicals, so that even the incomparably refreshing and palatable qualities of pure water from the well or spring are forgotten, or no longer treasured, except in old songs and chromos of the Old Oaken Bucket and the Spring in the Wildwood. The water supply engineers have discovered in recent years that it is *cheaper* to "purify" the water supply with chemicals, than to keep it pure with incessant labor and vigilance and safeguarding of the watershed. Over-treatment chemically of the water supply of towns and cities is now the rule, rather than the exception.

The belief, probably the most menacing to health, if not to life itself, among modern innovations due to science, that the refinement and denudation of the food supply carried out to increase the keeping qualities and hence the merchandising and marketing possibilities and reach of commercial foods, can be corrected or compensated for by reinforcement of foods (and medicines) with vitamins A, B, D, and whatever else offers commercial possibilities. Man's requirement of vitamin D is known to be small, and the increase of his intake to some unknown and almost certainly excessive figure through artificially vitaminized bread and milk, breakfast food, ice cream, yeast, and through endless dosage of man, woman, and child with cod liver oil and concentrates such as viosterol (both known to have poisonous properties) and haliver oil, is one of the newer perils of a subtlety unthought of even in the Middle Ages when slow poisoning was one of the more highly developed arts. The arts of the vitamin researchers have been quickly and profitably applied to the purposes of competitive advertising of vitamin-reinforced food substances, and at least two great universities are commercially involved in this highly disturbing development.

The belief that any scientist, whose own eating may be done at a college restaurant or boarding house or faculty club, is qualified to tell any grandmother with all the traditional skills and latent underlying science of a well-managed home and kitchen, how to choose the diet of young and old. With this effrontery goes the belief, all too commonly held among academic scientists (and not at all among their employers in the business world), that all knowledge is of equal truth and importance, whether the study be performed by disinterested scientific workers such as are still able to find employment at Cornell University and a very few other public institutions, or by business-paid food and health researchers under the canny auspices of the California Fruit Growers Exchange, a Standard Oil subsidiary, a Steenbock or Hooper Foundation, the makers of *Kellogg's Bran;* the Doughnut Machine Corporation, or the United Fruit Company, the dominant distributors of bananas. For this defection from sound science and common sense, the college professors who take the money, and the business men who allot it, must divide the blame.

The belief that any book-learning can be instantly and safely permitted to supplant every traditional knowledge and experience of food, which has by trial and error, over centuries, been incorporated into the mind and habit of the race. This illusion is due mainly to the work of teachers of home-economics and nutrition science, and of propagandists for milk, raisins, oranges and "protective foods," whose preparatory studies seem invariably not to have included anthropology, or any knowledge whatever of the place of tradition and racial experience in determination of an economical and wholesome dietary.

The belief that, for example, since experiments on a particular species of animal show that a certain carefully selected sample of fresh, raw spinach or lettuce contained a rich supply of vitamin C, everyone should promptly and whole-heartedly go over to a generous helping of raw pineapple, carrots and lettuce on every possible occasion, and take his dietary leadership from grass and clover-eating animals, rather than from human beings living in a natural and native culture. The experiments done on rats and guinea pigs have a curious way of being promptly carried over to human beings to whom with different digestive apparatus, different habits of life as to rest, play, mental strain, etc., they often do not in the least apply, or may even apply in reverse. The public must learn that the much-touted caution, and show-me attitude classically imputed to men of science is by no means an attribute of men of science on a ginger ale bottler's or flour miller's payroll.

And last, and very important, the naive belief that a government run by business men temporarily turned into cabinet officers and bureau heads, selected by a business-minded and business-advised chief executive, with huge investments in big industries and no training or background in consumers' rights or needs, will conduct *its* scientific experiments and give its scientific advice in the interest of the general public rather than in the interest of more profits and sales by food processors, brokers and chain store merchants. With honest, consumer-minded, and consumer-staffed government scientific bureaus, the harm of the false ideas and misleading beliefs already set forth in this chapter could have been confined in their worst effects at least to a limited group of illiterates or uneducable citizens, by the government's issuing a continual stream of truthful and well-directed and forthrightly expressed counter-propaganda. With the government as well as private experts sold out to business, and quick to fall in line with its great need for pseudo-science in furtherance of the exploitation of consumers and the masses who toil for a subsistence or less than subsistence wage, the great middle class who get most of their intellectual fare from *Good Housekeeping*, the *Cosmopolitan, Collier's* and the *Saturday Evening Post*, the *Chicago Tribune*, the *Philadelphia Bulletin*, the *Los Angeles Times*, the *Binghamton Press*, and the rest of our commercial press, are snared in the trap of words and pictures that have directly and indirectly made for the substitution on 20,000,000 home and restaurant tables, of baker's bread chemically adulterated and even chemically flavored, for genuine home-baked bread of fine flavor and savor; and canned corned beef hash with canned spinach, for a juicy steak with baked potatoes, baked squash, and fresh peas.

III

"PROGRESS" IN OUR FOOD SUPPLY —BIGGER PROFITS AND MORE PEOPLE SICK

The standard retort to critics of the package food manufacturer, of the restaurant keeper who serves inferior foods
(as all but a few do now), of the bottled beverage dispenser,
of the bottlers and canners of indigestibles like olives stuffed
with anchovies and capers, sausage with pistachio nuts,
goose liver paté with truffles, and maraschino cherries; of the
food advertising copy writer, and of the experts who advise
farmers to spray and to dust their truck gardens and orchards with ever increasing amounts of arsenic, lead, manganese, and selenium, is: What of it? Are not people still alive?
Aren't we, through the blessings of commercialization and
salesmanship, richer and better provided for than we used
to be? Isn't science enriching our lives with plumbing fixtures,
halibut-liver oil, vitamin cough-drops, metholated cigarettes, and radio broadcasting of crooners? How can any
red-blooded American doubt that we shall always be bigger
and better and grander than any other nation, and our national stomach better filled and more often filled with comes-
tibles? How can Americans, who invented mass production of
canned "baked" beans and soup, hot dog sandwiches, and
doughnuts, and the only nation successfully to turn oranges,
apples, cheese, wine, and fruit cake into factory products
with belt-line production techniques, be expected to believe

that one might learn more about foods and drinks from one's
grandmother than from realtors gone into the Sweet Shoppe
and Wayside Inne business, or New York stockbrokers
turned into California vintners?

It is quite in the American order of things that the very
business-like and dollar-centered section of society that is
most assured of the rightness of machine-made mince pie and
chemically preserved hamburger and "cheese-spreads," is
the section most vociferously against every move necessary to
the increase of taxes to support larger and more numerous
hospitals and sanatoria and more and more free medical
and dental clinics and rest-camps for the poor. No business
man processing alum-treated pickles, making jam of sulphur-
dioxide-preserved fruits sprayed during their growing period
with heavy doses of lead arsenate, or salvaging spoiled
canned salmon by a "reconditioning" process, so-called, under government supervision, will ever see the connection between the feverish and very costly research being done on the
causes and cure of heart disease, stomach ulcer, of strange
and terrible maladies of the skin, and of cancer,—and the
wider consumption of his shoddy and well-nigh uneatable
and certainly indigestible product. But a very real connection exists. The public health depends more directly upon
food—upon the *kind and quality of our food*—than upon
any other factor whatever. Any child knows that a person or
an animal fed on a grossly unsuitable diet, say of corn
flakes, canned beans, or factory pie, and drug-store ice
cream sodas will after a due interval, sicken and die. That
a person can safely consume only a limited proportion of
his total food intake in the form of such artificial and un-
healthful foodstuffs is not so well known, and for many,
what was once a fair margin of safety has become the bor-

derland of danger of physical breakdown and impotence. Corruption and sophistication of the diet is an insidious process like the conditioning of Germans by Hitler and Goebbels, for hatred of the Jews and for beating the drums for war. There is a little toleration of sulphurizing of dried fruits, then of ethylene treatment of fresh green oranges, lemons, cantaloupes, persimmons, pears, tomatoes, and bananas, so we can have "fresh, ripe fruit" regardless of the season or the unfavorableness of the growing conditions. Then comes the development, now widespread, of a *dyeing* process for green oranges to make them appear ripe when in fact they are still green and still indigestible. There is a little toleration of artificial coloring of butter and cheese which makes the product of unhealthy and stall-fed cows look like that of sleek kine on green pastures. All these devices steal away our common sense and sound dietary instincts, and finally we find people, even people with a college education and some knowledge of the sciences, allowing bran processors (who are making a market for a miller's by-product that even cattle can eat only in closely limited quantity) to determine the diet of educated and uneducated alike. The daily newspapers and the popular magazines help in a swelling chorus of pseudo-science and bunk to decide for them and for you and me that canned tuna, spinach and canned fruit salad, those next-to-zero's in fish, vegetables, and dessert, are suitable for human food—indeed for regular, daily use as human food!

Dogs, which living close to man have yielded up their dietary judgment to his, frequently sicken and die because they are fed badly selected, or artificial, or over-refined foods which do not agree with the requirements of their stomachs and intestines. Cats are more independent and tough-minded and stick to their own ideas of what is fit to eat. As a result, cats given any sort of fair chance to find the food they need, keep healthy and sleek, although to do so they may have to select carefully and knowingly from the best stocked garbage pails of the neighborhood and to make serious inroads on the bird and rodent population of the house, stable, and garden. Dogs, more trustful animals, more easily forget their hunting and raw meat instincts and are more likely to eat what is bad for them—*and* what would be bad for their masters.

A generation like the one just now coming to youth and middle age, is brought up to an extent which at times astonishes us, upon tinned meat, synthetic gravy, pastry made with canned fruit, glucose, and cottonseed and corn oil, factory-made sauces and flavors, bread that is unspeakably bad (that must be reserved for a later chapter for adequate description and condemnation), canned soup, even canned chop suey and chow mein, and apples, peaches, pears, prunes, and cabbage, cauliflower, celery, and broccoli that have been dosed heavily with terrible insect poisons to protect them during the growing period. One of these poisons (the one most commonly used) is so virulent that 1/45,000 of a pound daily will bring on symptoms of poisoning within a short time, and 1/4,000,000 of a pound is a dangerous amount for daily intake over a period of years. Hams and beef and bacon are cured (with the aid of injections by a syringe!) with strange chemicals more suitable as disinfectants for use on the bathroom floor than for food preservation. Perhaps as serious as anything mentioned is the fact that all sorts of vegetables, fruits, breads, cakes, and even meats are "enriched" and preserved and cured and canned and pickled with suicidal amounts of sugar and glucose and refined starches (the latter may become nearly as bad a food as sugar). Such artificial and over-sweet and over-pasty substances never were a part of the diet of man in his natural environment, and cannot *safely* be added to his food supply now or at any time in the next hundred thousand years.

To a certain extent the efficiency motive, distorted by the natural desire—under a profit system—for profits, has been at work to bring about these changes. Farmers come to grow the crops of grain or forage or milk or eggs in the kind and quality which bring them the largest *dollar* returns. Food processors, millers, grinders, bottlers, canners, restaurant keepers, tend to go into those lines of trade and to adopt those practices of their own group which enable them to buy and to process the cheapest raw materials in such a way as to produce the highest "value of product." The ideal business, as any business man knows, is one that permits him to buy something as cheap per pound as sugar, corn, corn-starch, flour, cheap shortening, phosphate, soda, cocoa or skim milk or some inexpensive combination of two or more of these, and sell something as dear as corn flakes, corn syrup, and cornstarch pudding, mixtures like pancake and waffle flours, *My-T-Fine*, and *Good Luck* Lemon Pie Filling, *Flako* Pie Crust, *Kre-mel Dessert*, *Bisquick*, and other prepared puddings; or as cheap per pound as wheat flour and sugar and cottonseed oil, and sell something as dear as baker's bread, cake, and candy that has wonderful "eye appeal" but lies like a weight in the stomach. Likewise, a specially favored trade, that of meat packing—so beautifully adapted to big business organization and exploitation that only a few huge firms are allowed seriously to compete for the enormous profits available—has the remarkable good fortune to buy fine cattle at 10 cents a pound on the hoof and see its steaks sold at retail for 50 cents a pound. Even its by-products (which by a farm housewife would be regarded as unusable waste fit only to feed to the hogs and chickens) are ground into a paste, tinned, and sold as sandwich spread or under some other unrevealing name at a price above 30 cents a pound. In the fish industry fresh mackerel has been known to go begging at 1 cent a pound wholesale on the Boston fish pier, only to appear a few days later in a big city fish market at 42 cents a pound! And what the meat or fish packer makes from his sales of hides and hair and blood and bones and glue sausage meat and casings, and offal used for cattle and chicken feed and fertilizer, no one can tell, and no accountant working in the public interest has set himself to find out. Consumers often think that public accountants work at the wrong things, and for the wrong employers!

Out of these complex economic drives, of the very existence of which the average man is blissfully ignorant, are built up the social customs and school and college teaching, the domestic arts, and the teaching attitudes of home-economists and dietitians, the "sciences" of nutrition, the economics of agriculture and marketing. The end result, to the farmers and to members of Congress and of state legislatures, just *seems* to happen to come out badly for the consumer—and for the farmer likewise. Many well-meaning and earnest people have thought and protested about this, and the *Congressional Record*, and hearings of Senate and House Committees record many millions of words of argument and protest on this shocking cheating of the farmer at one end of the chain and the consumer at the other, by business, and especially by big business. Yet the fundamental and radical cause and cure are never so much as touched upon, because to name the real cause of these abuses of the public's stomach and pocketbook would go straight to the heart of the problem of business under a profit system. Good products will not be produced and delivered to consumers in sufficient quantities under the profit motive, and the farmer will just as surely not receive a fair price for what he produces and delivers to processors. Business is business, which means that it is not a way, except at long last and incidentally, of supplying consumers' wants on the one hand and assuring purchasing power to producers on the other.

But the whole matter could not in fact come out any other way in a business system compounded of profit first, a wide diffusion of magazines and newspapers dominated by the interests of the same business system, a periodical literature which is "cheap" because it is most profitable to business to pay for the public's reading matter through advertising rather than to let the money come from direct payments by the readers. Other major factors that have betrayed farmers and consumers are a marked and increasing domination of the schools, of university teaching and scientific research, and even of research carried on by the government's own scientific staffs, by business through direct and concealed subsidies of the most far-reaching and subtle kinds.

With the effect of the radio on the public mind and upon the public's appreciation and understanding of good foods and good cookery, it is impossible to deal in the space of this book. Suffice it to say that the radio exemplifies in the minds of most social scientists and leaders of humane thought, the most astounding and shameless corruption and prostitution of a great public interest that can be envisioned in our generation. Men like Aylesworth and Paley have

made out of the radio exactly what the Hearsts and Bonfilses
and the Gannetts have made of the newspaper press, a very
good and very profitable business, and a very bad imitation
of a public service. So hopeless and so far beyond reforma-
tion are the outpourings on food and health matters on the
radio, and so unmitigated by any corrective forces or any
measurable minority of radio communication of a contrary
kind, that few above the moronic levels of the auditors of
sponsored (advertising) programs, take seriously *anything*
that is said or *any* advice that is given them. Those who do
believe what radio announcers and soup and canned beef and
macaroni pluggers tell them (and millions *do* believe such
rubbish for lack of any other medium of communication
adapted to their minds—and at the same time honest) are
simply letting themselves in for a disastrous future of ill
health and distress for themselves and their children. Surely,
anyone who pieces together any significant proportion of his
dietary choices from what he hears on the radio is paving
the way for eventual breakdown of health, and, if he uses
his mind too late, for a lifelong invalidism and hypochon-
dria. To get an idea of the general ethics of radio advertising and the general want of decency and lack of concern for
the public welfare in its broadcasts, readers would learn all
they need to know by listening to the current advertising
plugs of almost any of the widely exploited and advertised
food products.

The only substantial differences you will note between
most radio advertising and the palaver of the old-fashioned
medicine man who sold cure-alls and pain-killers from the
tail of a covered wagon, with the accompanying entertainment of a banjo soloist or a snake-charmer, is that the modern radio continuity is somewhat more subtle, and consider-

ing its wide reach, a good deal more irresponsible and reckless of its hearers' well-being than the old-time barker or spieler.

The attitude of the federal government under either the old deal or the New in tolerating such atrocious broadcast advertising as that of *Kolor-Bak* that "ends gray hair worries" and was not described in the honest terms of a hair dye, hazardous to some users, or the advertising of *Crazy Water Crystals*, is beyond contempt, and defies any adequate expression by this writer, used though he is to the operations of a New Deal government believing in giving more timely and better protection to "consumers" in the stock market and on grain exchanges, than to consumers at the drug store, the fruit and vegetable stand, or the grocery.

One of the most depressing types of individual one sees is the young person who has never eaten or does not remember the taste of homemade bread; or one who thinks canned soup or the average restaurant clam chowder or berry pie is fit for civilized people to eat. One young high school girl who went to the store in a country town to get a cake, and was offered a choice between a flavory home-baked cake and a cellophane-wrapped, elegantly-labeled, factory-baked cake whose predominant character was that of sugar and adulterated chocolate, came back unhesitatingly with the factory cake. That young person, already far from well, will never have the slightest idea, when she grows up into an ailing womanhood, that her health and the health of her husband and family simply cannot be built on foods that can only be made attractive and kept that way by being wrapped in cellophane—foods of a type that cats and dogs and mice would instinctively reject as unsuitable to sustain life. The baker's cake, bread, and pie involve almost no ingredients in their processes that a housewife would consider fit for cake or bread making: low grades of flour, made from low-priced wheat, whitened and artificially aged with chemicals to make it look like flour of kitchen quality, and to take up as much water in the finished loaf as possible so that water may be sold at bread prices; cottonseed fats instead of cream and butter; yellow coloring matter instead of eggs; unsanitary frozen and dried eggs instead of wholesome eggs at a higher price fresh from the farm; cornstarch and tapioca to fill up pies and pastries with a diluted bulk instead of real berries and fruit; chemicals like citric and tartaric acid instead of lemons and other fruit flavors. Here we see at work the standard process of big industry, of substituting the cheap factory-produced product like cotton oil or cornstarch or sugar or glucose for the dearer farm-produced product like cream or butter, honey, berries, lemons, peaches, or cherries. Every one of such cases costs the consumer nutritive value and value for his money, and costs the farmer the sale of a fresh product in a favorable market![1]

Many critical illnesses, a goodly percentage of which end in death, or permanent impairment of health, are due to poisoning from eating adulterated food. For example, very recently in Providence, Rhode Island, contaminated pastry brought about the death of two children, while more than 120 persons were reported ill. It happens that one of the two children who died had been a diabetes sufferer. It is a fact surprising to many that there are no provisions in our food and drug laws, state or national, which recognize any right of an ill person to be protected against grave injury

[1] From *The Consumer and The Farmer—Both Get Gypped,* by F. J. Schlink, reprint of radio address given over station WRNY, New York City, on April 4, 1933, available from Consumers' Research, Inc., Washington, N. J.

or death that may result from a food contamination or
adulteration that to a well person might be harmful but not
necessarily serious. The ability of the public to learn about
baker's pastry after a large number have taken sick, is clear
from the newspaper account of the Providence poisonings,
which remarked that "it was next to impossible for a baker
to sell cream puffs or eclairs in Rhode Island tonight."

In a later case in Westchester County, New York, the
brother-in-law of the county medical examiner had a serious
illness, much aggravated by the poisoned pastry which
caused the serious illness of some 800 to 1200 customers in
April 1935. The medical examiner, according to *The New
York Sun*, said that "if a death occurred he [the medical
examiner] would initiate an investigation to fix criminal responsibility." Some consumers will be interested to know that
medical protectors of the public health act as though criminal responsibility were something which begins "if a death
occurs." In Rhode Island the bakery business is less tenderly
treated, and the bakery which was the cause of the poisoning
at Providence was permanently closed, an idea which was
not even suggested or discussed in connection with the Westchester pastry poisonings with their much larger number of
persons affected.

Again, for those who think that the food poisoning hazard
may be an inconsiderable one, it is in order to mention the
case of canned salmon. Within very recent years the government has confiscated a number of lots, running into millions
of cans, found to contain adulterated (spoiled) fish. In a
court decision which went against the government bringing
suit against the canned goods (not against the packing concern, which was not even brought to trial), the judge re-

marked that "We must admit people may be expected to eat some putrid food."

Of one large quantity of spoiled salmon, 19,258 cases, or nearly a million cans, were of *Happyvale* Brand Pink Salmon (packed for Emery Food Co., Chicago) and *Rosedale* Brand Medium Red Salmon (Libby, McNeil & Libby, Chicago). Another part was unlabeled. In this case the Court followed a process which is quite regular in Food and Drug Administration proceedings of allowing the condemned food to be released to Libby, McNeil & Libby (under a bond of $6000) for sorting the good portion from the decomposed portion. The bond was to be cancelled upon proof that the decomposed portion had been destroyed by the packer in the process of separating the adulterated from the unadulterated salmon. Those who know their salmon but are not in the salmon business will have grave doubts of the feasibility of any such sorting and will be sure that from the consumer's point of view the only safe way to produce good salmon will be to pack only fresh and sound fish in the first place.

Yet these cases, shocking and dramatic though they be, are by far the *least* important result of food adulteration and the distortion of the diet which comes from the choices of a population guided by advertising and concealed product-publicity (see Chapters XII, XIII), and by home-economists and nutrition-scientists with strange but financially very profitable concerns for the prosperity of the milk and flour milling trades. Many diseases and weaknesses of muscle and nerves are caused by food adulteration. Food poisoning by arsenic and lead, discussed hereafter, and also familiar to all who have read Consumers' Research Bulletins and

100,000,000 Guinea Pigs are, as the pathologists put it,
protean in their manifestations. That is, they affect many
tissues and organs; they produce ailments and disabilities
that simulate a dozen dangerous diseases, and often defy
diagnosis for a long time.

Both lead and arsenic poisoning can produce baldness.
Two of the commonest manifestations of arsenic poisoning
are a kind of eczema, and urticaria. Obscure nervous ailments and muscular pains, which the doctor is likely to consider as merely imaginary or due to nervous instability or
undue willingness to yield to real or imaginary illness, are
the not uncommon results of poisoning by lead and arsenic
and other poisonous metals that contaminate literally hundreds of different kinds of common foods and condiments
and beverages. The end result of arsenic poisoning (*proven*
to have resulted from this cause) is all too often a skin
cancer. (Even cattle and horses die of cancer in smelter and
metal-refining districts where arsenic is disseminated as an
invisible smoke or powder through the air, often for many
miles from the furnace which is the source of the poison.)
Either lead or arsenic poisoning may bring about a general
breakdown of bodily functions including the gravest maladies or complete failure of the intestinal tract, and worse
yet, perhaps, both are very unlikely of detection or correct
diagnosis by the average physician, or indeed by any physician not exceptionally skilled in this unusual and special
field of medical research.

The general malaise of the population is difficult to prove
on any thoroughgoing scientific basis, because governmental
experts who are responsible for the presence of a large
amount of both these poisons and many others of a serious
character in our food and beverage supply, are not likely to

give publicity to any far-reaching proof of their own derelictions. Yet such general decay of health is evidenced not only by the greatly increasing prevalence of illness and insanity (which represent not merely more extensive hospitalization and medical care but a genuine increase of ill health) but by a number of habits of life which are increasing so fast as to cause general comment among medical men and even among school teachers and others who have an opportunity to observe the growing generation and the one just grown.

Typical of these are the continually increasing use of means of stimulation of tired nerves and aching muscles of a people generally (in the classes most evidently affected, at least) living an increasingly softer and easier life that should give them *less* need for palliatives: by cigarettes in endless succession; by more or less continuous drinking of coffee, liquor, and other stimulants, like *Coca-Cola;* by increasing use of sugar, and of candy, chocolate, and ice cream and sugary soft drinks as pick-me-ups; by the astonishing increase in the use of aspirin, and caffeine-containing stimulant tablets, and the hypnotic drugs, the barbiturates (such as *Allonal, Veronal,* and *Luminal*), and those strange and most diabolic inventions of the young moderns in the southland, the double-strength *Coca-Cola* and the *Coca-Cola* containing a dissolved aspirin tablet! It is interesting that the South, which has great numbers of *Coca-Cola* addicts, is also the region where the food supply of small towns and country districts is worst from the standpoint of nutritional balance, partly because income is lower, partly because the climate is more trying, and certainly in part because the critical faculties of the people are at a low level both by custom and education, so that more and more misleading advertising is believed and obeyed. *Coca-Cola*, corn liquor or apple jack,

and strong coffee come in pretty handy in a land, both North
and South, where the food is increasingly unsatisfying and
increasingly adulterated and more and more unpalatable and
indigestible, or bordering on the poisonous.

There are half a hundred restaurants and "Coffee Pots,"
so-called, along two avenues in New York City familiar to
this writer, where the food is so terrible, so tasteless and so
bad in its cookery, that if he were forced to eat it continually for a week of twenty-one meals, he too would be
driven to some sort of treatment to deaden the critical faculties and allay the pangs of hunger. Perhaps a mixture of
cognac, *Coca-Cola* and aspirin would provide the necessary
distraction! The cookery in most small towns, relying as it
does largely on canned goods, even for soups, salads, and
desserts, is almost uniformly bad, and the town where a
truly tasty, skillfully cooked meal is to be had in even one
public restaurant is coming to be a phenomenon, and people
write their friends of the find they have made on a recent
motor trip to Hackettstown or Skaneateles or, as is more
likely, Quebec or Mexico City.

America is a land of food cults. California, where religious,
economic and literary cults of strange kinds flourish, is also
noteworthy as the home of food faddists, and of nutrition
workers who find that certain poisons in our food are really
beneficial. But at root the person who takes up a food fad or
tries to eat "scientifically" and rely on the "protective
foods" that McCollum, Sherman, and other nutrition experts
talk of so suavely is but attempting to escape the obscure
and only vaguely perceived results either of a poor, tasteless, ill-cooked or adulterated diet, or of dietary indiscretions
or fetishes of his own or of his family. That is, food fads
are attempts at escape, usually of people of good income,

who are well off enough economically to be *able* to seek
escape from their ailments by a change of diet. (Food fads
find poor soil in countries where the native diet is natural
and good and unadulterated and prepared by cooks of skill
and art.) Food faddery, alas, provides no real escape from
the perils of bad food. The person who shifts to oranges,
lemons, and grapefruit, to acidophilus milk, cod-liver oil,
Kelp-A-Malt, Catalyn, raw vegetables, such as carrots, beets,
and cauliflower; dried raisins and apricots, and bran and
nut meats, in an effort to avoid the palpable adulterations
and over-refinements of the customary food supply, and of
commercial cookery, of atrocious home cookery or can-
and-bottle-opener "cookery," falls into a new difficulty and
tries to consume a diet which is not human at all, but would
be tolerable to only a limited category of herbivorous animals or, more often, of no category of animals at all. The
cow and the horse, whose chewing apparatus and digestive
systems are very different from those of man, would even find
unpalatable and debilitating the diet of many who think
they find their inspiration in the eating habits of herbivores
like the squirrel, the rabbit, and the deer, and of the fanatic
adult milk drinkers who find their inspiration in those of the
young calf and the very young kitten or rabbit.

From this rapid survey of the food problem of Americans,
we see that it is a pervasive one. It will shortly appear that
escape for even the well-to-do from the dilemma of bad food
and senseless dietary habits is for the most part impossible;
that the trouble goes to the roots of our buying and selling
civilization, and that its solution, if one is possible, lies in a
radical reconsideration and reconstitution of the goods,
processes, purposes and goals of our society. It is necessary
to examine the character of the "controls" that have deter-

mined Mr. Average Man's and Mrs. Average Woman's choice of food, the sudden, determined drive on milk, orange juice or spinach, and the practices and beliefs of those whose responsibility it is to teach nutrition and dietetics and to do research in food problems. It is of great practical importance to see who decides what *your* food habits should be to produce the greatest profits for growers, packers, canners, millers and bakers, and what instrumentalities of the schools, of commercial writing and advertising and of the "public" press these powerful groups employ to get control of the public's ideas about and customs of eating. A later chapter will show some of the results of some of these practices upon the pocketbooks and upon the health and well-being of us all; and throughout the book will appear numerous practical suggestions of ways to avoid to the limited degree that they can be avoided in a complex, closely interlinked commercial society, the traps and dangers that threaten the average consumer when he buys food at the grocer's, baker's, or butcher's or takes his chances upon a meal in a public restaurant.

IV

REFINED FOODS FOR OVER-REFINED PEOPLE

The habit of eating "delicate" foods is one of those automatic punishments which are applied to those who, in ignorance, or in disregard of age-old experience of the race, seek to improve on Nature. Certain it is that even in primitive societies, the hunger instinct, one of whose manifestations is to get food in concentrated rather than in diffused form, must have impelled men to the quick satisfaction and social distinction that came from easy access to concentrated foods like honey and the fat of animals. Certainly it is no peculiarity of "civilized" living that gorging with specially sweet or rich food results in a very severe, but educative bellyache. The man or animal that gorged himself with honey or fat fish in defiance of instinct or tribal custom, and paid for it in pain and regret, learned a lesson. Modern man, impelled by social custom to feed immoderately as to amount or as to kind of food, not on rare occasions of apparent good fortune such as the discovery of a bee tree, or a buffalo just brought down in the chase, but whenever he chooses to (if his income suffices) or whenever his friends and relatives or fond parents choose for him, learns no lesson from such an experience. He gets used to feeling bad, a little lumpy and a little unhappy in the regions within. His friends come in time to regard him as a bilious case or hypochondriac. Being frequently or continually somewhat indisposed themselves,

they see nothing seriously disturbing in a general feeling of
stomach or bowel discomfort—so long as it is continuous
and of a tolerable kind rather than volcanic or immediately
threatening a medical or surgical disaster.

Civilized man has in large measure avoided or postponed
the consequences of his wrong eating habits: he can retire
late and sleep late on occasion, whereas his primitive forebears had to be on with the trek, the hunt, or the canoe
building, or whatever else the continued food supply or
safety of the tribe required. Modern man, hopeful as always
of improving on nature through "progress," can and does
take bicarbonate of soda, *Ex-Lax, Cascarets, Pluto Water,
Kruschen Salts, Crazy Water Crystals*, or *Alka-Seltzer*, or
anything else the radio "education" of the moment, paid for
almost entirely by business enterprises of the less honorable
or less socially necessary kinds, tells him is the proper special
mode of evasion for his diet problem. If the need of relief is
desperate he can call a doctor and perhaps get absolution
for his sins in the form of a colonic irrigation. At any rate,
he has means of avoidance and evasion that were wanting to
his primitive forebears whose medicine men were often limited to charms and incantations where their modern suc-
cessors have tools and potions, almost specialized, one might
say, to the necessities of the badly fed or indiscreet eater.

In early societies where nearly everyone—not merely "the
masses"—often shared scarce and scanty rations, dilutedness
or bulk of foods was associated naturally with a limited food
supply or limited labor power to hunt or to grow foodstuffs.
On the other hand, the richer and more powerful, as they
acquired position and prestige, were able to skim the cream
and reject the milk, eat the choicest and fattest bits of meat,
the most delicate and succulent vegetables, and rare and

fragrant fruits and wines. In later times, this eagerness of the "upper classes" for the cream of the food supply has resulted in the amazing and dreadful dietary menaces of canned paté de foie gras, rich cream soups, lobster à la Newburg, filet of anchovies with capers and pimentoes, fat roasts of pork and beef, avocado salad (among the very highest in oil or fat of any fruit), and such fat-and-sweet dessert combinations as honey layer pastry, rich shortcake and sugared cream, chocolate éclairs, mousse, pudding with hard sauce, frozen eggnog, and a whole new series of extremely rich, sweet, and indigestible desserts specially designed for home-manufacture in the upper middle classes' electric refrigerators. Indeed, a large proportion of the desserts eaten by the upper-ten group in any urban community is so rich in sugar and fat that such desserts are in almost the exact category, so far as diet hazards are concerned, as candy. As will be seen in the later discussion of baker's goods, the worse and more scientifically commercialized such "foods" as baker's cakes, pastry, and factory ice cream for the hotel trade become, the more they approximate sweetmeats (safe to consume only rarely and in the smallest quantities) and the less any proper sort of food. Recent publications have related the experience of a restaurant chain when it adopted the new policy of all-you-can-eat, permitting repeat orders for any item in the meal without extra charge. The second helpings were not of roast beef and mutton chops, but of "ice cream on apple pie, more peach shortcake, and another chocolate éclair."

The craze, representing in the main a quite unconscious instinct for delicate and savory or sweet and fat values, at the cost of essential nutritive values, has been enormously helped to the great cost of the health of millions—by the shrewd publicity of candy manufacturers and of the Sugar Institute, which invaded even the publications of the American Medical Association. It has been especially aided by the dietitian's and home-economist's wholly irrational delight in the "science" of Calories.[1] Judged by the Calorie touchstone, which is a measure of the *fuel* value of foods and is not even a correct measure of the fuel value of the food as actually burned *in the furnace of the body*, white sugar and cottonseed or coconut oil receive the highest ratings! As foods, each of these is an atrocity, alone, or even if combined in any considerable quantity with other foods.

The feeling that the white and shiny is a "nicer" (since less common and less available) food than the dark and lus-

[1] The vogue for Calories has pretty well died by now, yet one of Columbia University's leading texts, *Feeding the Family* (Dr. Mary Swartz Rose, Macmillan Co., New York, third edition, 1929, reprinting of May, 1935), devotes well over a hundred pages of a total of 450 to the substantially useless and now discredited Calorie tables, and to food pictures showing Calorie values. Incredible energies were spent at the well-nigh useless task of computing Calorie figures for "⅘ cup apple snow," "1 cup of citron, dried chopped," and "1½ chocolate drop cookies, 2¼ inches diameter," "⅗ cup turnip greens, creamed," "sundae, vanilla ice cream with walnut marshmallow sauce," and "rice fondue on saltines." The Calorie era of "nutrition science" is fast fading now into the "protective foods" era, in which everyone must drink milk and eat lettuce because of something the flour miller left out of the flour and something the fruit grower did to the oranges by spraying them with arsenate of lead and then picking them green. Worse still, children and adults are now required to eat a protective food like oranges or tomatoes because another protective food, milk, has deficiencies due to stall-feeding of cows, grand-scale distribution practices, and the pasteurization which makes them possible. Some bright home-economics student should ask her teacher how far the process of finding protective foods to protect other devitaminized so-called protective foods must go, before something fundamental and rational ought to be done about the whole question of food-supply degeneration determined by the profit drive that stops at nothing.

treless, is of course at the root of the vogue for white meat of
chicken and for all sorts of fowl and shellfish and other fish
that have a white or creamy color; for white beans as against
black; for light-colored eggs as against dark; and worst of
all for the population, for white bread as against yellowish
or dark gray or brown bread. One of the first and most
universally accepted signs of a rise in social status for a
poor family is its escape from the class of those who must
live on black bread or rye bread into the sacred company of
the millions who live largely on the dead-white bread of the
commercial baker, or the yellow-dyed fancy breads and
sugared and dyed coffee rings, cinnamon buns, and the like
that go with the next level of income and social position—
up in the Buick-Culbertson income classes.

The *National Butter and Cheese Journal* in January,
1935, noted that where the Jewish population is large, light-
colored butter is coming into favor. In time such almost
colorless and flavorless and, to an epicure, unattractive butter will come to displace the naturally colored yellow butter,
as white flour has displaced gray and brown. Southern markets, it seems, like a deeper yellow butter (probably because
this color is popular and accepted in corn bread), while
eastern and northern markets like their butter light in tint
and free even from the nuances of flavor that distinguish
good butter from any oleomargarine. As will be noted in
another place, the color of butter is, through governmental
approval of butter-dyeing, no longer a measure as it once
was, of its vitamin value, so that, given the going customs
of commercial adulteration, the light-butter New Yorkers
are, in point of fact, little if any worse off than the dark-
butter Southerners.

Dark color of food betokens generally richness in impor-

tant dietary factors other than mere fuel value (as to the
latter, richness is measured chiefly by fat, starch, and
sugar content); and so, by the increasing trend toward
refined-looking foods, we are effectively working ourselves out
of nearly all of our dietary margins of safety. The white-
meat, sweet, faintly flavored Washington or Oregon apple is
little but sugar, water, and "bulk." The apple strongly colored within, and the crab apple, with a tang and a complex
flavor, is almost certainly the one that should be preferred.
Likewise, with brown sugar as against white; yellow squash
as against white; black beans and peas and lentils as against
light-colored ones. The very things we lose by the shift to
the refined and pretty foods are the things that safeguard
our teeth from decay, keep our blood, bones, and tissues in
the best condition to resist invasion by disease germs and by
metallic and other poisons, and, perhaps more important
still, are effective toward health by helping us to keep *down*
the intake of foods rich in fuel and poor in almost everything else, such as sugar, cooking oils and fats, like *Crisco*,
Wesson Oil, or *Cottolene*, refined starches, "Cream of
Wheat," white corn meal, white bread, cake, and sweetmeats
of any color. And the more such foods are eaten, the more
plausible become the arguments of those who offer for sale
vitamin concentrates, cod-liver oil, irradiated bread and
milk; the more necessary, likewise, like noxious medicines to
a sick man, become their toxic or mildly menacing wares. It
is surely nonsense for anyone to deprive himself of the vitamin and mineral values in natural foodstuffs and then to
"correct" the damage by going on a regimen of dietary
adjuvants or crutches like cod liver oil, viosterol, *Bemax*
(and numerous other cereal-germ concentrates), carotene-
containing cough and cold medicines, mineral-rich but rela-

tively indigestible foods like spinach and kale, and so on *ad infinitum*.

Aside from the charm of whiteness, blandness, and delicacy of tint or flavor, the strongest possible drive exists toward the denaturing and hence whitening of foods in order to increase their "durability." The bread and cake and cheese that keep best can be set down as almost certainly among the ones which serve least well as food, or may even feed one in a way unfavorable to health. The whole trend of modern food processing and food packaging is (for what are to the processor and packager sound economic reasons, and to the farmer, the consumer, and the government very *bad* economic reasons) toward:

(a) Package foods that are ready to sell without further manipulation or weighing or packaging, and hence, because of the irrational supposition by the purchaser that distinctively named products have distinctive characteristics, make difficult or impracticable the substitution of one trademarked product for another. Thus they assure the processor his brand monopoly and the corresponding *extra* price he can charge for his goods as compared with the undifferentiated or bulk commodity formerly bought.

(b) Foods that keep indefinitely without decay, loss of flavor (if any!) or infestation by insects. It is not an accident that foods and food accessories which keep well, such as hams and bacon, corned beef, baking powder, white flour, dried cereals from corn flakes to bran, are the high profit items that satisfy the grocer because his function in selling them is reduced to almost exactly that of a slot machine which passes out a "unit" or container, and takes in money and rings it up in the cash register. Other common "imperishables" now pushing good foods out of the market are

dried fruits treated with sulphur dioxide, oranges wrapped
in paper and coated with wax, mineral oils, or borax; process
cheese (near-cheese now displacing genuine cheese almost
everywhere, even in the homes of people whose forbears knew
Roquefort, Edam, Camembert, Brie, Gorgonzola and Stil-
ton), condensed milk, gelatine and cornstarch desserts and
pie fillers, and a great variety of canned meats, fruits, and
vegetables. No longer does the container hold a net pound or
quart—often or usually it is a short-weight pound or a
short-measure quart, pint or half-pound portion of jam,
or "fruit-spread" or a pasty substance resembling cheese
expensively enveloped in tin foil or cellophane.

Set down this principle as a fair safeguard. The food
that is best for A&P, or Liggett's soda-lunch counter, or
Woolworth's food department, is also a great boon for the
firm that buys cheap raw materials from the farmer, shovels
them into a lot of very expensive machines, employs a very
few low-paid shovelers, conveyermen, handle turners, machine
watchers, and truckers, and sells the resulting product,
beautifully packaged, as English biscuits, fancy crackers or
canned beans to a food broker or wholesaler, at a tremendous markup. The ideal food from the business point of view
is flour mixed with a cheap baking powder, phosphate, soda,
glucose, powdered skim milk, and other cheap ingredients,
and sold as a pancake flour or a biscuit mix. This technique,
by which farmers are persuaded to buy back their own products at hugely inflated price levels, "gave advertising a
chance to prove its power, and realized $50 per barrel in-
stead of $7." *Advertising and Selling* so described General
Mills' three specialty products, *Bisquick*, *Wheaties*, and
Softasilk, by which advertising was used "to maintain earn-
ings . . . despite a sharp drop in physical volume." Like-

wise with candy, which, aside from the packaging, costs not
much more to produce than the car-lot cost of the sugar and
glucose which predominate in its makeup. Candy made according to the formulas accepted by the trade, and properly
shellacked with floor varnish or other glazes or wrapped in
cellophane, will keep for months or years on the merchant's
shelves, and easily sells for 30, 40, or 50 cents or more a
pound to a person who forgets the price of sugar, and who
has not stopped to think that a food which keeps so well as
candy and so beautifully and permanently resists the attack
of insects and bacteria must be a long, long way from the
kinds of food commonly eaten by healthy and vigorous men
who are close to nature. The kinds of food eaten by primitive
man and his babes were no sooner made available by slaughter or threshing, or harvesting of the orchard than they
started to spoil, to take on the odors of decay, and to be
assailed by moulds, bacteria, insects, and even rodents, in
numbers and kind beyond the powers of man, even today, to
control (except by poisoning the food with ethylene, or
cyanides, or sulphur dioxide, or benzoate of soda, or by other
disadvantageous changes in the kind and mode of preparation of the food in question).

Food that keeps well has certain limited uses; for the
traveler who journeys in the wilderness or must pass through
the canned-goods-cookery regions of any state, "durable"
foods may, as a small part of the diet or as a stimulating
beverage, be a practical necessity. But the hunter or fisherman who goes into the wilds on a store of chocolate bars,
baking powder and biscuit flour, and dried fruit and canned
beans, had better be sure to catch his fish or bring down his
game, else the durability and portability of the convenient
foodstuffs in his pack will be a poor substitute for the steaks

and potatoes and chops and fresh fruits and vegetables he might have had at home.

It would be hard to sum up this problem of refining and sophistication, denaturing and devitaminizing of diet in more clear and authoritative fashion than was done by the eminent English physiologist, Leonard Hill, in the 13th edition of the *Encyclopaedia Britannica* in the article on "Vitamins," who makes these strong statements on our modern dietary:

"A mixed diet of fresh meat, milk, butter, eggs, fruits, honey, molasses, vegetables and wholemeal bread, such as our ancestors ate, supplied all, but now this food is largely replaced by the products of the miller and canner, by white bread and polished white rice, cornflour, sago, tapioca, tinned meat, sterilized milk, sugar, margarine made out of nuts, egg substitutes, tinned or bottled fruits. Tea, sugar, white bread, margarine, and low quality jam are the staple foods of the very poor [in Great Britain; the foods of the very poor in the U. S. A. are nearly but not quite as bad]. The effect of preservatives and refining processes has been to lessen the vitamins and essential salts, often with disastrous effect to growth, health and breeding power. Now the growing of salads, which might be possible in gardens and courts, in window boxes and on roofs in cities, is stopped by smoke pollution; this, too, damages the fields, gardens and allotments, and lessens the supply of vegetable food and of milk of cows fed on fresh young grass, and makes these things costly to city people."

Again, Dr. Lafayette B. Mendel, physiological chemist, writing in the *Journal* of the American Medical Association of July 9, 1932, commented on the amazing diversity of the diets of our ancestors of two centuries ago, and the equally amazing dominance of fresh meat, game, and fish in the menus (a single San Francisco bill of fare of 1851 listed 46 choices of meat, fish, and game dishes; an English clergyman's *breakfast* menu of 1855 included four meat dishes and one egg dish; an 1847 hotel menu included meat and game courses and a few items besides, which merely to name would nearly fill this page). Dr. Mendel remarks the conspicuous omission from such bills of fare of the "refined or processed edible materials that have been developed through the efforts of the food industries in the last few decades. This," says Dr. Mendel, "is notably true, for example, of the numerous highly milled cereal products and other cereal novelties that have come to take a conspicuous place in the American meals of today."

In another place, Dr. Mendel remarked, in 1927: "The fact that one-fifth of our diet, nowadays, consists of vitamin free food is especially important because the other four fifths have also lost much of their vitamin potencies in the refining processes to which so many modern foods are subjected. Cornstarch, for instance, is a purified food; the vitamins and salts of the maize kernels from which it is made have been taken out. Rice, in the process of polishing, has lost most of its vitamins, and the same is true of other highly milled cereals. And not only the carbohydrate foods but also the fats and even some of the proteins in our diet are being subjected to chemical 'purification' before they reach our kitchens."

The tissues of the body which show perhaps the most noticeable and troublesome effects of refined and "civilized" foods are no doubt the teeth. There is an extensive literature on the relation of tooth decay (dental caries, as the expert terms it) to the devitaminization, demineralization, and over-refinement generally, of common foods of civilized races.

From this intricate and detailed literature, only a few typical quotations can be given in the space available.

Dr. Russell Bunting, in *Science*, Nov. 10, 1933, says: "It is a well-known fact that dental caries is distinctly a disease of modern civilization. The natives of Alaska, Newfoundland, South America, the South Sea Islands, Africa, interior Europe and Asia who live segregated lives quite remote and untouched by modern civilization are almost wholly free from dental caries. When these people adopt civilized life or move into civilized communities their children become highly susceptible to dental disease. In a study of the essential differences between uncivilized and civilized life which might be related to the prevalence of dental caries the most outstanding characteristic is that of diet. As long as primitive man lives on the simple foods which are indigenous to his locality, he has little need for a dentist, but when he adopts the white flour, sugar and canned goods of civilized life he and his children invariably are stricken by dental disease which is often more severe than among civilized communities."

Dr. A. Gault, in the *Journal* of the American Dental Association for May, 1934, says: "The food of these people [the Fijians] consists of fruit, vegetables and fish, and has done so since their arrival in Fiji, and where this diet is still maintained, there is little doubt that the dental conditions are much better than that [sic] of those nearer the towns, who follow the diet adopted by the average white person."

Books have been written to prove that the human race simply cannot get along without milk. The Fijians evidently could. The best known of the books treating milk as essential to bodily health is Dr. Tobey's book called *MILK the Indispensable Food*, where the very title of the book per-

petuates the fallacy. Incidentally Dr. Tobey (B.S., LL.B.,
M.S., Dr. P.H.) is, and was at the time of publishing the
book a paid employe of the *Borden Company* and editor of
the *Borden Digest*. It is interesting that advertising in connection with this book did not stress the fact that Dr. Tobey
is not a physician nor a nutritionist, or that he received
professional training as a lawyer and is rated as an expert
on public health, especially tuberculosis, and public health
law. He is the author of some four hundred articles and nine
books, in many of which he has done yeoman service for his
employers, though without mentioning their profitable interest in his very favorable attitude toward milk.

It will be of interest to those who insist that milk is an
essential of the diet to build good teeth and prevent tooth
decay, to note that Dr. Gault reports that "Fijians [whose
dental troubles are recent] have never used milk in their diet
until recent years."

Samoans, too, are shown by Dr. R. A. Ferguson of the
U. S. Navy's dental service to have remarkable freedom
from tooth decay if left in their native environment, whereas
their susceptibility to tooth decay is markedly increased in
the presence of altered diet, and upon mingling with another
race.

In the predominantly meat eating Eskimos, "The significant fact," says Mr. (Henry B.) Collins (Jr.) in *Science* of
March 25, 1932, "is that in remote, barren regions of Alaska
to-day where the Eskimos are poverty-stricken, they still live
in the old-fashioned way as seal hunters and fishermen. And
the . . . Eskimos practically do not know what toothache
is like. But Eskimos living in proximity to white settlements
show a much higher incidence of dental decay. At Nome, for
instance, we find more than half the natives with carious

teeth. In the teeth of those Eskimos who supplement their native sea food diet to a greater or less extent with food that the white men eat, dental decay is prevalent and is directly proportionate to the extent that the diet has been altered. . . . There is evidence that meat-eating races generally have sound teeth, while grain-eating races are much more affected by tooth decay."

That it is not merely primitive living and the consequent use of rough and ill-prepared foods that are responsible for this phenomenal difference is made clear by other material in ample amount, of which the following must for the present suffice. Mr. Collins goes on to say, "Indian tribes who lived along the sea coasts of America left great mounds of shells showing how much sea food they ate. These tribes had almost perfect teeth. The buffalo-hunting Indians of the Plains had fine teeth. On the other hand, the Pueblos of the Southwest, both ancient and modern, and other agricultural tribes of the United States have poor teeth. These Indian farmers lived mainly on grain and vegetable foods."

The tooth paste advertiser's assertion that his tooth paste (*Ipana*, for one) must be used to overcome the dreadful handicap of modern soft diet is thus shown to fall into the same category as the rest of the attempts of advertisers to marshal science to the consumers' undoing. Only persons with a commercial axe, or tooth brush, to grind, could fall into the illogicality of ascribing tooth trouble to soft, prepared foods, and ignore the basic difficulty of the civilized diet, which is the defects of its constituent substances, and the fact of the extraction of essential food elements—to enrich the diet of horses, cows, and chickens. Others who benefit with the barnyard animals are those fortunate human beings who are economically well off enough to be able to purchase in the form of dietary additions, such as wheat germ, rice polish, etc., the very substances whose removal in the first place, at the consumer's cost, made the purchase of the extra ingredients plausible or necessary. Civilized men and women are, so far as known, the only category of human beings who pay the makers of white rice, white flour, macaroni and breakfast foods like Cream of Wheat and puffed rice to take out an essential food substance, and then pay the same or another group of business men to sell the extracted ingredients back to them again in the form of wheat germ, and rice and wheat bran. The final absurdity consists in the activities of the Bureau of Home Economics and other tax-paid experts who recommend the use of rice polish (for example) to supplement inadequate and poor diets, without daring to mention in their recommendation, on pain of losing both their jobs and their Bureau's congressional appropriations, the social and scientific absurdity and indecency of uneconomic manufacturing and marketing arrangements which have brought about the extraction of these indispensable and scarce food values in the first instance.

Mrs. Mellanby, who with Mr. Mellanby is responsible for the epochal discovery that use of cereal foods (bread, crackers, cakes, "breakfast foods," porridge, etc.) tends to produce dental deformity and tooth decay in and of itself, remarked that, ". . . in spite of the excellent work of dentists there was more dental decay than ever in the world." This discovery, the most important perhaps in the history of nutritional science to the health of 130,000,000 Americans, has gone almost if not quite unnoticed in Department of Agriculture food science circles, including the Bureau of Home Economics. That Bureau is not of course a true scientific or home-economic bureau but is in many respects a branch of the farm-products marketing activities of the Department of Agriculture.

It was true moreover of tooth decay that educated (i.e., miseducated) people suffered more than natives living their primitive life. To continue, quoting a very brief digest of one of Mrs. Mellanby's numerous, and (abroad) highly regarded and everywhere quoted papers on this subject, ". . . when . . . natives came into contact with civilization their teeth began to suffer. The Eskimos had beautiful teeth—only 3 per cent were said to suffer. The primitive Negro of the tropics had white pearly teeth free from decay, but his descendants in the United States were almost as prone to dental disease as Europeans. Mrs. Mellanby said that wrong diet (mainly deficiency of vitamin D) and lack of sunshine especially in early life were the primary causes of caries and pyorrhea. Cereals, including oatmeal and maize, were harmful and anti-calcifying foods. The Eskimo had good teeth because in his natural condition he hardly ate cereals and his diet was rich in animal fat, with which vitamin D was associated. It was true that the diet of natives in tropical countries included much cereal, but most of, if not all, their skin was exposed to the sun's rays and the necessary vitamin was synthesized in their bodies. Dental decay was prevalent in countries such as England because cereals were the cheapest food, there was little sunshine, and what there was was not allowed to play on either the body or the food."

Curiously, the change of American agriculture which this discovery should be bringing about would be very much to the farmer's economic advantage, but the Department of Agriculture, whose experts have spent much of the public moneys familiarizing themselves with the experiments of

other scientific workers abroad, do not care to discuss re-
orientation of agriculture on the basis of a lower grain consumption. The Secretary of Agriculture does not dare to
face the problem of lower prices for the farmer's grain, even
though less consumption of grain would mean the greater
consumption of other more expensive farm produce requiring more acreage and hence exactly in line with the present
alleged principles of the Agricultural Adjustment program
of the New Deal. The farmer, under decreased grain consumption, would get lower prices for grain (which is already
being reduced in *production* in the hope that consumption
will hold up or increase) but a higher total income from his
crop, which would include more fruit and vegetables, and
above all more meat animals, poultry and eggs.

Dr. Weston A. Price reports in the *Journal* of the American Dental Association, finding in the Isle of Lewis, in the
Hebrides, old and old-fashioned people, unillumined by the
light of home-economics and the commercial food and restaurant business, continuing to eat their original *traditional*
diet and still in possession of fine teeth. Among the younger
generation supposedly informed by superior schooling in
health matters and having access to the refined, whitened,
and devitaminized food supply of commerce, it turns out
that dental disease is rampant.

The moral will for some be clear. The process of making
money is a process of making money *out of consumers* in
more ways than one. Truly when Humpty Dumpty's diet fell
off the wall into the hands of the millers and bakers, and
makers of breakfast food, ice cream, candy and soft drinks,
it was left in a state that will defy a lot of putting back
together by dentists and dental clinics, by *Adex*, viosterol,
Bemax, *Vegex*, and preparations of brewers' yeast, by scien-

tific research at Columbia and California and Wisconsin and a score of other great institutions of light, and as Chapter XI shows, all too often of misleading.

It would be hard to sum up the great speed at which we advance *backwards* through work of subsidized or incompetent food scientists better than by quoting briefly from the discussion on sulphur dioxide treatment of dried fruits in *100,000,000 Guinea Pigs*, p. 243:

"The scientific editor [of the Department of Agriculture] also emphasized, as a complete justification for sulphuring, recent researches showing higher Vitamin C content of sulphured fruit as compared with fruits dried without benefit of bleach and preservative and failed to state that this vitamin, present in raw dried fruit as fed to the laboratory animals, is lost in the cooked dried fruit which is fed to human consumers; and the cooking is necessary to assure proper sanitary quality and digestibility, as well as to eliminate a portion of the sulphur dioxide. And note these two sentences buried in eight pages of text in the California researchers' paper, and not referred to by the editor of scientific publications: *'The only abnormality observed in the animals fed the sulphured fruit was a slight chalkiness and brittleness of the incisors* [front cutting teeth]. These are now being examined chemically and microscopically.' While it is hardly safe to assume that laboratory rats suffer as much on a diet of poisons as do human beings, we cannot see why the animal nutrition experts of California are so willing that human beings eating California dried fruits should suffer any degree whatever of 'chalkiness and brittleness of the incisors' in order that the fruit sulphuring industry may suffer no loss of dividends. If their fellow scientists will put no restraint on careless reasoning from healthy rats to men and women, many far from healthy, we may hope that such consumer influence as can be brought to bear in university affairs will teach these researchers a reasonable respect for the rights of consumers in California—and elsewhere."

As to the reliability of instinct, once the safe guide of man and animals through the infinitude of choices at one time or another offered the hungry creature by a bounteous nature in woodland and plain, Ellen Richards, the mother of home-economics, who did her thinking a generation ago and long before the days when food *manufacturers* were dominant in control of our dietaries and our high school and college home-economics teaching, said: "It is unsafe to trust the individual to the guidance of the appetite alone, for the reason that this instinct was built up for a condition . . . very different from that which enables the people of this country to indulge themselves today."

Unwise indulgence in canned beans, the chocolate éclair and the Boston Cream Pie, the marshmallow fudge sundae, canned-peach bakers' pie à la mode, chocolate candy bars, strong coffee, will never be brought under control of our instincts. To the extent that industry and advertising in the mass journals of home affairs and cookery (what little is left of it) read by the millions cannot be brought under social control, the few hundred thousand who sense the problem of food manufacture and selection as something that can no longer safely be left to dominance by commercial interests, and to commercially oriented federal and state departments of agriculture, will do well to get back as fast and as far as possible to the food types and the food cookery of four to ten generations ago. In those times, when bleached, refined, highly-milled, and denatured foods were not used, adulteration was common only in the food eaten by city dwellers, chemical analysis and synthesis was still an unexploited science, and the food supply was in general safe because incomes did not suffice for the purchase of many boughten food supplies, especially those produced by remote business and big business. Chiefly the people's protection lay in the fact that nearly everyone retained through indoctrination from babyhood a native culture in which sound habits of food selection were among the most important items of belief and behavior transmitted to the growing generation.

Before Minneapolis, there was good bread. Before Irradiated Milk, canned cooked macaroni, canned Boston Brown Bread, canned wieners and canned corned beef hash, there was good food and safety in the pleasures of the table; it is in the customs and home manufactures of those older times that we must seek the foundations of health in the diet of man living in civilization.

V

MEAT—THE FOOD MAN EVOLVED ON

Bloodthirsty though man is, and cruel and ruthless in many of his manifestations of power, including the various organizations of professional patriots, a Georgia prison camp, an association of anti-labor employers in San Francisco, and the army officers who, for themselves, die comfortably in bed, most members of the human race show evidences either at times, or pretty much at all times, of pity toward their fellow men and toward the higher animals. It is curious indeed that cruelty toward other men, and especially that manifested by indifference to and neglect of the poor and the defenseless, is frequently associated with exceptional care for horses, dogs, cats, birds, or flowers. Psychologists know that the exaggerated concern for the comfort and welfare of animals or of potted plants is an atonement for a subconscious awareness of a cruel or exploitative attitude toward other human beings. One way in which this atonement drive frequently finds outlet is in a leaning toward vegetarianism, or a tendency to avoid the eating of meat or of certain kinds of meat. Thus many mild vegetarians think that it is proper to eat some meat, or some kinds of meat, as fish or perhaps poultry. Many do not follow the Roman church's view that the unborn child is as sacred as the baby, and hence find the eating of eggs far less objectionable than the eating of chickens.

It is pretty clear that the common preference of some food-conscious laymen and of many physicians for white meat of fowl rather than the dark, and of the meat of fowl rather than the red meat of cattle and sheep, is but a veiled avoidance of the idea of cruelty associated with the shedding of blood. There is no known reason why the meat of chicken or duck should be more desirable food than that of cattle and sheep; for many indeed, fowl will be less digestible and in any case it will be a less complete food for human beings (while a more satisfactory food no doubt for the birds that feed on other birds). Savages often have such a complete lack of qualms about the shedding of blood, that the drinking of the blood of animals forms an important part of the diet or of religious ceremonial; certainly such a foodstuff, or beverage if you prefer, would seem nutritionally desirable. Primitives also, lacking ice and cold-storage facilities, are wont to eat their meat while it is still warm from the kill, a practice that is also desirable nutritionally, however much it may go against the civilized, or over-civilized, taste of epicures.

There is hardly any topic on which medical men and nutrition experts have expressed such wide divergence of opinion as on the problem of meat-eating versus cereal-vegetable-fruit-eating. Clearly the "experts" have been led and often still are, through their unawareness of the primitive taboo element in avoidance of meat eating, to the idea (sometimes openly expressed but more often implicit in their writings) that much eating of meat is unfortunate and undesirable. There is perhaps an economic element in the question for many, and for some, who take the money of the baking and milling industries for the writing of testimonials and pamphlets favorable to white bread, there is an obvious bias in the direction of the pocketbook. There are some who realize, unconsciously perhaps, that under our present economy of scarcity (quantity and quality limited to what can be sold at a profitable price), much eating of meat, at least of good meat, by the masses is an impossibility. Farming tends, as already noted, under customary economic drives, to go over to the production of maximum calories; and home-economics and nutrition teachers with their economic drive largely determined by the good will and moral and financial support of the farmer, and of cereal-processing industries, duly and dutifully write books and great parts of books around the Calorie idea, and inevitably suggest the greater desirability of high Calorie foods, particularly cereals. Protein foods, especially meat, fish, poultry, and eggs, are treated by many writers on foods as a sort of necessary evil, and all sorts of rationalizations are invented and paraded to explain what cannot be explained (since originally the distrust of meat arises in an unconscious or unrecognized taboo against blood and killing, and later in economic motivations also, as already noted).

There is the rationalization that meat causes intestinal poisoning because it putrefies in the intestines; a fantastic theory if there ever was one, and supportable only by the purely verbal expedient of dealing with the breakdown or decay of starches and sugars and cellulose (bulk) under the nicer word, for those who like it better, fermentation. One gathers that nutrition experts like Dr. Mary Rose and Dr. E. V. McCollum, who talk of the putrefaction of meat and eggs in the intestinal tract, have never been close to a warm garbage pail containing a week old accumulation of canteloupe rinds, grapefruit and orange skins, spoiled milk, and old lettuce, those "harmless" substances that are supposed to exert so benign an influence on the intestinal tract. Says Dr. Rose: "Sometimes large amounts of protein food, espe-

cially meats, tend to increase intestinal putrefaction and
bring on a whole train of unfavorable symptoms; sometimes
the kidneys' powers are overtaxed, and certain compounds
of nitrogen tend to accumulate in the body to its disadvantage. . . . These purins [in meat] are not nutritious, but
are gradually transformed in the body to uric acid, to be
carried off as waste in the urine. Persons inclined to gout
have difficulty in getting rid of uric acid, and the more meat
they eat the more uric acid tends to accumulate in the system, circulating in the blood and depositing in the joints.
. . . Meat proteins are also particularly liable to intestinal
putrefaction, while milk not only is less liable to this kind of
decomposition, but actually helps to decrease the number of
putrefactive bacteria in the intestines. . . . Even athletes,
for whom meat was once thought especially necessary, have
demonstrated the possibility of reducing their daily consumption to one-sixth the amount which the training table
previously provided, with an actual increase in their capacity
for endurance. Aside from questions of health the economic
advantages of some other protein foods over meat are easily
demonstrated. . . . The housewife who provides a somewhat
varied diet, ample in fuel value, including milk and eggs, need
not feel that she is depriving her family of any essential if
she furnishes a very small amount of meat or none at all.
One-fourth of a pound a day as an average for each adult
man will provide approximately one-third of his protein requirement; bread, cereals, fruit, and green vegetables will
furnish another third; and the remainder can be obtained
with little difficulty from a glass of milk, an egg, some cheese,
beans, or nuts."

Had Dr. Rose acquainted herself with the general state of
health and energy and above all the "halitosis" of people

who are predominantly milk and starch eaters, for reasons
of miseducation or prejudice or enforced frugality, she might
have been less prone to follow the conventional view that
meat is bad, or to be eaten in limited quantity while "protective foods" like milk and leafy vegetables are ever to be
emphasized in the diet. Why nutritionists as Sherman, Mc-
Collum, Rose, and Mendel fall obediently behind the propaganda for increased use of milk and other protective foods
and spend so little of their energies in behalf of a dietary
complete enough and natural enough to need no protective
measures (as traditional and primitive diets do not, except
perhaps for women during pregnancy and lactation or for
persons recovering from serious illness) remains to be examined in another connection and as a problem in the economic
determinisms of science and the scientific worker.

Had Dr. Rose given thought to the fact that milk is a
desirable food for *young* rather than adult animals; that
overuse of bread and cereals is well known, by physicians
and dentists and by *English* nutrition workers, to be con-
ducive to tooth decay (see Chapter IV); that "green" vegetables such as kale, chard, spinach, cabbage, and lettuce are
far too rough for the average American stomach ruined by
a generation of eating according to a totally false set of
nutritional theories; that cheese and beans and nuts are
foods whose proteins are incomplete and hence require con-
scious balancing or supplementing with other and better
foods, and for many, perhaps most, are too concentrated
foods to go well with regular intestinal activity, she might
have been less glib in her disposal of meat as a food undesirable except in minimal quantities. These rather long quotations from Dr. Rose have been given only because they are
typical of (and equally as misleading as) nearly all the pro-

fessional nutritionists now writing on problems of food selection; they represent the views of the advanced or scientific nutritionists who have gone in so heavily for rat experiments on abnormal and narrowly limited diets that they have quite forgotten the commonplaces of the average man's eating and of the lesson of primitive man's simple mode of life and of food selection, and his abounding health, when left alone and free from implantations of nutritional science and raw salads, canned goods, candy, and baker's bread.

For an intelligent and unbiased view of these problems, we need to examine the opinions of those who write on the problem of protein less from the extraordinarily class-limited problem of gout mentioned by Dr. Rose (a disease of the aged and sedentary, over-eating and over-imbibing rich) and more from the standpoint of the enormous majority of the population whose incomes now prevent them from ever getting *enough* of satisfactory proteins, on account of the general overuse of milled and refined cereals, of dried and canned beans and vitamin-less or vitamin-poor fats (*Crisco*, *Wesson Oil*, refined olive oil, and the rest), and for whom even a minimal amount of *good* meat is as impossible of attainment as are diamond stomachers, Corots, antique spinets, and country estates guarded, as is Mr. J. P. Morgan's, by ex-marines and motorcycle policemen.

It is in order first to dispose of the view of Rose and others that hard work is better done on a diet low in meat and high in vegetables. Wishart, writing in the *Journal of Physiology*, 1934, page 189, found that "in prolonged hard muscular exercise the best performance is obtained on a high calorie diet rich in protein of animal origin"; it was his view that only from protein-rich animal foods (in which class are meat and eggs—and *not* milk) can a large supply of energy be obtained in small bulk and palatable form. An attempt to secure a really high protein diet from vegetable sources was a failure owing to the digestive troubles evoked, and this experiment showed the poorest performance of all. (It is well known that peoples whose poor or limited food supply forces them to live on a diet predominantly of vegetables and cereals, including many savage tribes in lands that are over-populated or poor in fish and game, show a tendency towards large abdomens and digestive troubles due to the large amount of material which it is necessary for stomach and bowels to handle in order to separate the absolutely necessary nutritive material from the large total quantity of food materials eaten.) It has also been shown that the metabolism rate (metabolism is the rate at which the body converts food intake into energy; a lowered metabolism commonly goes with poor health, impaired vigor, and lowered muscular, mental, and emotional activity) of long-time vegetarians is distinctly below (12 to 14 per cent) that of persons who eat a normal diet.

From the standpoint of evolutionary development of man, however, and neglecting special cases of persons requiring medical care with a particular choice of food, practically all the signs point to the desirability of large amounts of meat and animal foods (other than milk and milk products—for the problem of milk see Chapter XIII) in the diet. Green plants preceded the evolution of animals, just as herbivorous animals preceded the carnivorous. For man and other car-nivorous and omnivorous animals, the herbivorous animals, including cattle and swine, poultry, and of course fish, per-form the valuable service of sorting and assembling from the more elementary substances consumed by insects, worms, larvæ, building up the essential amino acids from green plants, grain, seeds, hay, insects, etc., animalculæ, yeasts, molds, etc. (Of these amino acids necessary to health at least 22 are now known.) Some of these are present in some vegetables and cereals, and some in others and in milk. The animals that are used as food by man also act to concentrate the otherwise very diffuse and diluted fat-soluble vitamins (A, D, and E) (H. Wu, *Journal of Oriental Medicine*, 1929, Vol. 11). Thus, for example, by eating the sun-drenched microscopic plants that are found at the surface of the summer sea, cod and other fish perform the function of concentrating the sunlight vitamins for those who are not able to work or play in the sun themselves or who, living in dark, foggy and cold climates, or wearing clothes on a body that in nature was meant to be naked, do not absorb as much of the sunlight as the body needs for health.

The Chinese, who on account of enormous overpopulation of their land, must derive more than 90 per cent of their energy from vegetable foods, are, according to Wu, notably inferior in physique and resistance to Americans, whose diet is only 60 per cent vegetable. "The digestive organs of the vegetarian must work much for little and this probably accounts for intestinal disease which, as a cause of death in Japan, surpasses even tuberculosis. . . . Vegetarianism, as a doctrine of nutrition, has no advantage whatsoever, except as a corrective of over-eating. . . . With an increasing population there is a greater tendency for man to farm his land so as to give the greatest yield in protein and calories (cereals and legumes) and it is this fact which makes for an increasing involuntary vegetarianism." (From an abstract of Wu's paper in the *Bulletin of Hygiene*, May 1930.)

As to the medical man's fads and fancies about diet, the

Journal of the American Medical Association wisely said
editorially (July 21, 1934, page 190): "The practice of
medicine has always been rife with ideas, fads and fancies
about diet. . . . Extreme complexity marks present practices because of the many discoveries in the science of nutrition and the resultant stimulation of food fads and miscon-
strued theories that defy [and evidently need] extermina-
tion. The physician, since his advice carries weight with his
patients, had been blamed not only for the perpetuation of
many old ideas about nutrition but also for the adoption
of many of the present unsound dietary practices and food
fads. Among the topics for criticism are the unwarranted
attacks on meat because it is 'hard on the kidneys,' the
'magic password autointoxication,' and the 'psychically
pandemic acidosis.' . . . Scientific articles on nutrition
should replace the syndicated food fad columns in daily
papers and discourage the adoption of fanatical and pseudo-
scientific diets."

A few quotations from an article by L. M. Hussey, writing in *The New Republic*, will throw light not only on the
problem of meat-eating, but also on the dilemma of the
growing, absurd "over-scientization" of diet.

". . . but faith in another spring-time practice [other
than sulphur and molasses] still persists. This is the belief
that all greens are of outstanding value to health, especially the first greens of the season. Those who can babble
a bit in scientific phrases say that the greens add iron to the
blood.

"Presumably, then, we pass through the cold season with
little or no iron in the food and we make up the deficiency
by consuming the green shoots that appear in May and
June. Recent investigations show that neither of these sup-

positions has a basis in scientific truth. The common foodstuffs of winter are by no means wanting in factors that
can add iron to the blood, and, on the other hand, a number of greens and chlorophyl-carrying vegetables have no
value in adding haemoglobin to the corpuscles.

"As iron-producers, beet-tops, for instance, are perfectly
inert. So is celery. So is parsley. . . . Of the common
greens, spinach is about the only notable iron-producer. It
is, however, probably surpassed, late investigation indicates,
by articles of common winter diet such as red meat and
butter fat.

". . . there is scarcely an adult person who at one time
or another has not taken some controversial stand on the
question of meat and a meat diet. Of all dietary superstitions, the notion that meat-eaters pay usuriously in ill-
health for the steaks and chops they consume is, doubtless,
the most profoundly rooted. Within certain limits, it is a
superstition that has even been persistently upheld by medical opinion, and has gained a measure of support from
scientific investigation. Particularly, generations of practitioners have held that at least one of the contributing causes
of kidney disease, or nephritis, was 'a high protein diet.'
Since meat dishes, above most others, are rich in those food
factors called 'proteins,' this is much the same as declaring
that a liberal use of meat poisons the kidneys and brings on
their dreaded degeneration.

"Again, as certain meats are the progenitors of uric acid,
there came about a second grave indictment of flesh eating.
For it was believed that uric acid was the direct causative
agent of those nerve, muscle, and joint symptoms lumped
together under the convenient name of rheumatism. Worse,
the meat eater, if that unhappy individual chanced to be

a nursing mother, might presumably poison her child as a consequence of dietary error, for an English investigator, working experimentally with nursing rats, was able to show that the milk of these animals, when fed upon a high protein diet, became poisonous to their young. . . .

"Further light has recently been thrown on the question of kidney disease. Since this ailment was presumed to result, at least sometimes, from an over-use of meat, the diets prescribed in the past for nephritis aimed at 'resting' the kidneys by reducing the number of meat dishes put upon the table. Now in all sufferers from kidney disease it is very well known that there is a loss of protein—in which, as was mentioned a moment ago, meats are peculiarly rich—in the form of albumin in the urine. This abnormal presence of albumin in the urine is, indeed, a chief means of diagnosing the ailment. . . .

"Here we have abnormal losses and an impoverishment of the blood. In short, here we have losses of an important food constituent which must, if the patient is successfully to combat his illness, be replaced. Thus the doctrine of 'resting' the kidneys by reducing the amount of meat on the table is seen to be an error. The whole principle of feeding in nephritis has been, in certain cases, reversed.

"As for the uric acid theory of rheumatism, study of the complex phases of that disease has so far disposed of uric acid as the cause that we seldom hear the substance mentioned any more. [Compare the views of Dr. Mary S. Rose, who still shares in the scientifically obsolete terror of uric acid, as appears in the quotation on page 82.] . . . The conditions that may give rise to rheumatic symptoms are startlingly numerous—but none of them, so far as investigation can discern, has anything clearly to do with meat.

"What, then, of the chance of poisoning a nursing infant by permitting the mother a heavy meat diet? Such a poisoning, remember, has not been demonstrated in the human child. It is an inference drawn from experiments with lactating rats. With these animals it was shown, as mentioned a moment ago, that a diet rich in proteins produced poisonous milk. By a rather natural course of reasoning, the poisons were referred to the excessive proteins in the food mixture. However, a later study of the constituents of that food mixture shows that its excess of protein had nothing to do with the unpleasant results. These were a consequence not of too much protein but of too little of a certain vitamin. . . . Again, foods rich in protein—in short, meats—have been acquitted on another count in the indictment.

"The whole debated question of meat-eating finds an illuminating commentary in the experiences of Stefansson in the Arctic, as related lately by Dr. C. W. Lieb in the Journal of the American Medical Association. Stefansson has observed the dietary habits of the Eskimos over a long period of years. He has watched those whose diet is almost exclusively one of flesh and others who have adopted a mixed diet, including imported foods. He declares that among the meat-eaters of the Eskimos there is no undue nephritis, no excessive hardening of the arteries and no curtailment of life. And in his own case he has been unable to observe symptoms of disease as a consequence of the almost exclusive use of meat over notable stretches of time. On the other hand, the mixed diets and reduction in meat seem to injure the people of the Far North. Stefansson says that the recent use of imported foods by the Eskimos appears to bring about many of the ailments of middle life that are so common in the civilized nations.

"From this one must not leap to the conclusion that the correct diet is, after all, exclusively flesh and that one digs one's grave by reducing meats and adding other foods. Before reaching any conclusions it would be necessary to study the sorts of additional foods now sent to the Far North. But one is obviously safe in observing that a whole race of people can eat meat and nothing else—and survive in good health. The appetite of the individual is doubtless often fallible as a guide to correct diet. But with all the uncertainty of present knowledge, it is perhaps a better guide than unsupported prejudice, or the indications of premature reasoning from partial investigation.

". . . Milk, for instance, is a food toward which the faddist turns ever the fondest gaze. Heavy milk diets have been proposed as a cure for virtually all diseases; they are still prescribed for tuberculosis without any positive evidence of their value—all this in spite of the fact that milk is enormously rich in calcium, has a calcium content far beyond the needs of any adult animal that is no longer developing bony tissue [and a mineral or vitamin substance present far beyond the body's requirements is often, as in the case of copper and vitamin D, to give but two of many possible examples, actually poisonous to him who consumes it— FJS]. . . .

"That, indeed, [referring to the much advertised superstition that yeast is a cure for skin blemishes] sums up the character of most of the food fads, present and past. They are charms, they are amulets, they are the products of the witch doctor. A bit of pseudo-scientific abracadabra and thousands are ready to believe and eat accordingly. So it is proved that the last witch was not burned at Salem."

It is evident that had Mr. Hussey's paper reached a wider

audience, and had he written somewhat more fully on the subject, the present book, so far as it concerns the pseudo-science behind milk-drinking and not-eating-meat, need never have been written.

Rat experiments, by the present author freely admitted to have most serious limitations as an indicator of human diet, have shown, contrary to the misleading findings of 30 years ago that deceived Dr. Rose and others, the *superiority* of a high-meat diet (and its freedom from toxic effect) compared with a diet derived largely from plant sources. The superiority referred to was in growth, reproduction, secretion of milk by the mother rats, and duration of life. The original experiments (1907) referred to in the recent quotation by Mr. Hussey as at fault, are disproved by subsequent experiments of Hitchcock in 1926, on rats and also by experiments on 400 infants and their mothers. High protein diet in these experiments gave better milk secretion; high caloric diets (sugars, fats, starches), while increasing the mothers' weight, gave *decreased* secretion of milk. The later rat experiments—confirmed, as animal experiments should be, whenever possible, on human subjects —show only too clearly the dreadful effect of dietary knowledge and home-economic teaching based on too scientific or too theoretical experimentation by nutrition experts with superstitious fear of purins and intestinal putrefaction. (These experts are quite indifferent toward the fermentation associated with carbohydrate feeding and fermentation *and* putrefaction of milk and milk products, which habitually escape notice when food cultists and dietitians talk about the putrefying bacteria that thrive in the intestinal canals of carnivorous human beings.) Dr. Rose advises a dietary to avoid the supposed toxic qualities of meat, and quite ignores the known and proven toxic dangers of lead arsenate on fruit and vegetables, and those of cod liver oil, which she treats in her best known book as an indispensable and wholly safe adjunct of the diet.

Says Dr. A. F. Kraetzer, a leading expert on dietetic fads, in *Esquire* for March, 1935, in an article "Don't Eat What's Good For You": "Everybody thinks that it (intestinal toxemia, or autointoxication) is due to meat. It is due to nothing of the sort. It is due in the vast majority of cases to carbohydrates. Carbohydrates come from vegetables. They include sugar, starch and cellulose, the last named being the roughage that we have become so mad about. . . . It is a very significant fact that when the two Arctic explorers, Stefansson and Andersen, subjected themselves to the experiment of eating literally nothing but meat for a year, the putrefactive bacteria, which are supposed to thrive on such a diet, practically disappeared from their intestinal tracts.

". . . And, ah! that fermentation! [of carbohydrates: starches, sugar, and cellulose]. Not a genial kindly product by any means, but a fermenting mash that contains everything that makes bad booze bad, without benefit of ageing or distillation, the triple concentrate and inner essence of headache and low spirits. Many poisonous things are formed in our insides from the excess sugar that we take for energy, the superfluity of fruit that we take for vitamins, the detestable spinach that we take for roughage and iron. The things that we take because 'they're good for us.' . . .

"It is a very curious thing how our propensity for taking thought has led us astray on the subject of protein foods, meat, fish and eggs. Unquestionably we have built up a

prejudice against animal food and the origin of this prejudice is lost in prehistoric time. It has no sense to it. It
has all the ear-marks of some semi-mystical and highly primitive tribal tabu. Possibly it was an outgrowth of the early
ban on the taking of life. But whatever the original reason
for the prejudice it has been forgotten and its place has
been filled by a number of plausible rationalizations, some
religious, some hygienic, and all of them lacking the ability
to withstand any kind of searching criticism. . . .

". . . It is true enough that meat must be limited when
gout has once been established. But that does not mean that
meat caused gout in the first place, because it didn't. It was
something else, and inasmuch as beer and wine, those products of carbohydrate fermentation, are very probably factors, it may be that the excess carbohydrate that we eat because it's good for us may play a part as well. . . . And it
is the carbohydrate in excess that causes the intestinal
toxemia which we falsely ascribe to meat."

As to the quantity of protein from meat and eggs required for good nutrition, there is increasing agreement
among medical men based on experience with human behavior on high-protein diets, and a growing tendency to
distrust the laboratory experience of nutrition workers on
animal experiments of limited scope and bearing. The best
present opinion holds that there should be a greatly increased use of meat and other high protein foods (a far
greater increase than is conceivable for the great majority
of the population, considering the failure of our economic
system to distribute income in accordance with dietary
needs—and hence to distribute adequate amounts and proper
qualities of the meat, fish, cheese, and eggs which go with the

good income received by about ten per cent of the population).

The actual need for protein is highly variable, no doubt with the individual, and of course with age, nature of work, physique, habits, and personal taste. An official conference of British governmental experts and organized medicine recently came to the conclusion, among others, that "Growing children and expectant and nursing mothers required relatively large amounts of first class proteins [which is not the kind vegetarians get!], much more than would be arrived at by simple calculation based on man-value equivalents."

It is proper to say that to get the kind of meat one should have for a diet high in meat is difficult for all but the very few who live very close to sources of supply, for nearly all commercial meat and meat products are grossly adulterated and increased in weight with fat, by special feeding processes which increase the salable weight per animal or per fowl. Good meat, for most healthful eating, is chiefly lean meat of the kind that is produced by deer or wild cattle, rabbits, squirrels, or game birds, living in the wild where their flesh runs more to muscle than to fat. The overfattening of meat animals and fowl is but one of the endless variety of adulterations produced by the profit drive. "Adulterations-on-the-hoof," as they might be called, are one of the kinds that farmers themselves chiefly indulge in, because the government grades, as with canned goods, favor those qualities which maximize returns to producer and processor, and give low grading to those characteristics that favor the consumers who must eat the product. Millions of housewives have resented the large waste in their meat buying represented by the fat that must be thrown away; few have known that that waste was produced by the farmer and passed on by the packer by the connivance of federal and state governments and university agricultural schools and experiment stations for the precise reason that it forces the consumer to pay at meat prices for fat that he has little or no use for. So long as government stimulates the production and sale of corn and cottonseed oil and fat, and dairy fats, it has no moral right to press constantly, as it does through its meat and poultry grading systems, for increased production by farmer and packer, and subsequent waste by the consumer, of meat fats, which are paid for in bacon, ham, roasting beef, lamb, and pork, and chops, exactly as though they had desirable food values and were usefully consumed. If consumers will fight for the more economical and more natural lean meats, they will get them, and the meat and poultry grading systems will be run less for producers and more for those who must eat the product.

As to the potential damage of meat-eating to the kidneys, whose function is responsible for the removal of the products of the digestion and burning in the body of the meat eaten, the results of an enormous amount of experimentation are inconclusive, and examination of the available findings indicates little to support the older view that large use of protein foods have a harmful effect on the kidneys. Since the question of potential harm to essential organs often resolves itself into a problem of compromise between two evils and since Americans nationally suffer extraordinarily from bowel troubles and the damage done by cathartics and bran and agar and mineral oil and the rest of the panoply of offensives against bowel complaints, it would appear that an increase of load upon the kidneys (even if that were a concomitant of a diet high in animal proteins) and a decrease of the strain upon and irritation of the intestines would be in the direction of progress. This is especially in point for a nation which must get its home reading in the household magazines, its radio entertainment and its roadside eyesores in the form of billboard advertising to a large extent by the courtesy of vendors of intestinal accelerators and irritants. *Milk of Magnesia, Ex-Lax, Texas* and *Crazy Water Crystals, California Syrup of Figs, Eno Salts,* and *Feen-A-Mint* are too much with us. It looks more than a little as though the bowels rather than the kidneys had come to be a dangerously weak point in the American physiological armor. But more than that it is quite likely that the whole idea that meat puts a special load on the excretory organs is just one of those superstitions carried down from pre-scientific medicine, and pre-scientific nutrition, with their beliefs that uric acid crystals caused rheumatism, and meat and eggs caused acidosis that had to be overcome by "alkaline" foods such as milk, lima beans, and almonds.

Another important element in American nostrum-vending —that of weight-reduction medicines and regimens, from *Marmola* to the "Hollywood Diet"—points strongly to the need for a national shift, so far as a changed mode of income distribution to permit it is conceivable to our political and agricultural leadership, from starches and refined fats and sugars, which especially fatten (and interfere in other important ways with the body's normal processes), to fresh lean meat, poultry, and fish and eggs, which supply energy and satisfy appetite without greatly increasing the waistline.

VI

RAW VEGETABLES—FOR COWS AND HORSES

There are many reasons why the customary raw foods are not well suited to human diet in civilization. One is the great danger of bacterial infection. Living herded up in dirty cities, and the necessity of eating food handled in bacteriologically and hygienically uncontrolled markets and fruit and vegetable stores both make for grave risk to the person who eats raw lettuce, raw cauliflower, raw cabbage, and other fruits and vegetables that when used raw cannot have their surfaces completely removed (as by peeling) before they are eaten. In Paris, where for economy the water of the Seine was pumped into mains for washing of fruits and vegetables in the markets, diseases associated with infected water (such as typhoid) were common. Poisonous spray residues, discussed elsewhere herein, are another danger of raw fruits and vegetables. They are a danger, too, with cooked foods; but the risk of getting arsenic, lead, and other poisonous metals into the system is considerably decreased with the cooking of fruits and vegetables. Unfortunately valuable mineral and vitamin substances are lost too, along with the arsenic and lead, when one discards the water used for cooking vegetables—the very substances that used to be counted on to balance the diet safely against the losses of vitamins and minerals involved in pasteurizing milk, milling white flour, polishing rice, and using white sugar and canned meats, fruits, and vegetables.

The epidemic of amebic dysentery which caused many deaths in Chicago and other cities was carried by raw foods, and cold meat and salads cut and handled by infected persons. Moreover, moist human fecal material is used to some extent for fertilization of truck gardens, and under a profit-controlled producing and distributing system, government officers do not even dare to carry on a system of inspection and control of individual farms and gardens, or even of education of farmers and gardeners in matters directly affecting consumers' health and safety (though any degree of supervision of farm operation seems in order when an increase of farmers' income is at stake, as under the AAA). In the absence of any such inspection, it is absolutely impossible for any given person to be sure that his cabbage or lettuce has not been grossly contaminated by human fecal matter or animal excretions of a potentially dangerous character, either at the time of growing or handling. Amebic infections are most likely on raw fruits and vegetables from "California, Mexico, Tennessee, Florida and, in fact, most of the Southern states." (*Journal of the American Medical Association*, November 18, 1933, the article on "Amebic Dysentery.")

Pin worm infections, which are very common, especially in children, are also held to be increasing, due probably to growing use of raw fruits and vegetables.

Many argue that raw food is more natural than cooked; that those who urge a less civilized and less sophisticated food supply and believe in the necessity of reversion to a more primitive system of diet must accept the principle of raw foods. But this is an argument on insufficient information. Primitive man ate raw meat in great quantities; in some regions he lived almost exclusively upon a diet of raw fish.

Anyone could eat raw meat now, if it were freshly cut from a fresh-killed carcass of a healthy animal; but one does not safely eat meat which has been held for months in cold storage, or was shipped in the dirty and foul hull of a steamer from the Argentine, or in freight cars of which the housekeeping is far from that of the kitchen, or meat that was handled by dirty and hurried workmen who are driven by demands for output rather than by the requirements of sanitation and hygiene. Besides, much meat and poultry, especially canned meat, and poultry, are notoriously *not* from healthy animals.

Raw vegetables certainly formed no significant part of primitive man's diet; raw grains and seeds seem not often to have been extensively consumed, and where cooked or baked cereal grains were much used, the health of the population was notably inferior to that of primitive groups whose dietaries consisted predominantly of meat or fish or eggs. On the other hand, raw fruits and the few vegetables which would be substantially important in the food supply in the raw state, would, when grown in a state of nature and away from cities and sewage, be as free from dangers of infection as any food man could eat. But in civilization, and in civilization at its present high peak of accelerated production and *relatively* reduced social and technical control, almost nothing raw and nothing unpeeled may safely be assumed fit to eat unless one knows the conditions under which it was raised, and sees it harvested, transported, and handled thereafter up to the moment it is brought to the table.

As to the supposed health value of raw foods, it is startling to discover that pigs fed on cooked potatoes throve much better than those fed on raw potatoes, and not only made much greater gains in weight on the cooked potatoes but

preferred the cooked potatoes to the extent that they ate
nearly two and a half times as much of the latter as of the
raw ones. The cooked potatoes were more than twice as
efficient, moreover, as a foodstuff to produce pork. This report of the Agricultural Experiment Station at the State
College of Washington (January 1934) is typical of the
extent to which theories about nutrition of farm animals
are checked by actual experiment for the very practical reason that the farmer as a producer and seller of commodi-
ties will not tolerate half-baked information that may cost
him losses of money and crops. He must know that what he
is doing and that the forage he is feeding will be effective
for the purpose, and economical. It is only when consumers'
problems are involved that ridiculous and highly theoretical
assertions are allowed to go untested and yet be put into
practice in diet kitchens, relief administrations, commercial
and college lunchrooms, home-economics classrooms, and the
like. Human nutritionists unfortunately are permitted to
promulgate their pronouncements at will on the basis of the
thinnest experimental and deductive studies, in which even
the criterion of successful feeding—that of maximum rate
of growth of the young animal—is at long last found to be
a false one. (See discussion of this fallacy in Chapter XI.)

The home economists are much to blame for the vogue for
raw fruits and vegetables and for excessive use of raw salads.
The Bureau of Home Economics of the Department of Agriculture sends out a running fire of advice in its mimeographed bulletins and releases to the press to feed more raw
stuff to children and grownups, quite ignoring, as home
economists are wont to do, the grave bacterial and spray-
residue hazards, and the roughage hazard to delicate youthful insides. "One trick," says the Bureau of Home Eco-

nomics, "is to use some vegetables raw as often as you can
—in salad, or in slices or sticks, as if they were celery.
Then you get all their best food values, and also a crispness
and a flavor which peps up the rest of your meal. Serve
carrots, turnips, cabbage, or onions raw sometimes." Such
advice is plainly given in complete ignorance or carelessness
with respect to infections by eggs of intestinal worms or
bacteria, or protozoa, or coatings of arsenic, lead, copper,
or mercury on such raw vegetables as cabbage and lettuce,
and quite without regard to the digestibility of the raw
food. This blithe carelessness with the health of their clientele is all too typical of home-economics workers, not only in
the government departments in Washington but also in universities, experiment stations, and in other institutions
where home-economics courses are given, and pamphlets and
bulletins are written. Consumers' Research has had wide
contacts with home economists. Its technicians have read the
professional literature of home economics for years, but the
organization has known so few who have been able to see
the important relationships between such matters as the supposed desirability of raw food, and the alarming findings of
experiment stations and of Consumers' Research on arsenic
and lead residues on fruit and vegetables, that the layman
is advised to disregard home economists as sources of trust-
worthy information on food questions. No one need look
to home economists to relate the insistent recommendations
of raw fruits and vegetables for all and sundry, with the
artificial ripening processes now in almost universal use
which have set us all unknowing to eating green oranges,
bananas, pears, cantaloupes, and tomatoes instead of fruits
which naturally ripened would have been fit for people of
good digestion to eat in their raw state. A number of home

economists have even criticized Consumers' Research for calling attention to the dangers of lead and arsenic residues and of the artificial devitaminization of foods. Such talents as they have had have been almost uniformly exercised in the direction of suppressing unfavorable criticism of food industries and food processing and of the growing over-commercialization of the mechanics of the food supply.

Home-economics neither is an honest art of cookery based, as all great arts are, upon the tradition and experience of the race, nor does it exemplify the beginnings of a genuine science of food supply. The home economists *should* have read such papers as that by J. T. Smeall in the *British Medical Journal* where yeasts, colon bacteria, and staphylococci were reported on about half the samples of raw fruits examined. The happy, untroubled pollyanna outlook of home-economics teachers prevents their ever discovering or discussing the unpleasant factors in the food supply; the infestations, infections, and the spray residues that are just as important an element of an apple or a lettuce leaf as are the supply of "precious vitamins," minerals, and roughage that are stored within. The author suspects that as the palatability and savor of foods have decreased, there has been an unconscious attempt on the part of home economists and their newspaper and magazine clientele to make up for this fundamental loss by an unhealthy and unscientific emphasis upon color, arrangement, decoration, napery, and silverware, and crystal goblets for those highly undesirable carbonated beverages which noted home economists and nutrition workers misleadingly recommend as important and desirable factors in the food supply.

It is quite probable that the home economists' vogue for raw salads has much to do with their notable and frequently

absurd predilection for "beauty" as a substitute for substance at table. A four-page mimeographed bulletin boost-
ing raw salads, from the Bureau of Home Economics, falls
into the standard domestic science patter: "To begin with
one of the prettiest salads you can think of, put one or two
green curling leaves of new cabbage . . . cottage cheese
with chopped peanuts mixed in." In correspondence the official leader of the American home economists, Dr. Stanley,
admits that "the possibility of infection from the use of raw
salads is, of course, so great in certain areas as to prevent
their use. In general, in this country, the chances of infection are not great, except in the case of foods like watercress, which may be grown in infected streams. This can be
avoided by the use of mild antiseptic solutions which are
available for washing these." The bulletins recommending the
use of raw foods, and these are as frequent as they are unscientific, maintain an unbrokenly cheerful attitude and do
not mention the unpleasant circumstance which comes out in
the correspondence quoted, that in *some regions raw foods
are found too dangerous for their use to be feasible*. Dr.
Stanley's statement that the danger can be avoided by the
use of mild antiseptic solutions is an incorrect one and dangerous to her clientele. A competent bacteriologist of whom
inquiry was made on this point states: ". . . the business of
making infected watercress safe with a little antiseptic washing is certainly unsound and unsafe. I certainly would not
recommend the use of any vegetable, including watercress,
grown in a stream known to carry infection or to be polluted
by sewage. There is absolutely no justification for growing
or using food stuffs known to be infected even though an
attempt is made to disinfect. Of course disinfection in the

case to which you referred would be very incomplete and highly worthless under the conditions stated."

A German physician, in the days before Hitler's ascendency, summed up the situation very well when he said: "Good cooking is considered to be one of the present-day essentials in every German household and institution. The craze for raw food should not be indulged." Home economic journals in America and elsewhere please take note!

VII

A SURVEY OF FOOD FADDERY

It has already been noted that Americans are abnormally susceptible to food fads and cults. The advantage of the faddist approach to the problem of food selection and preparation is that during the period for which the particular fad remains in vogue, it ceases to be necessary to use the mind. Like the religious basis of fundamentalism or Holy Rollerism, when once the fad has been selected, the responsibility can be left on the lap of Providence. Good effects, if any, are the results of the change of diet; bad effects become, as it were, acts of God, and beyond human intervention. Some of the fads, like the acid-base balance idea that alkaline foods should be eaten in preference to acid-forming foods popularized by the eminent Dr. E. V. McCollum of Johns Hopkins University and heavily supported by nutritionists at Columbia University and other institutions, including the Bureau of Home Economics at Washington, had the most reputable of "scientific" origins. That the science that went into its devising was a partial and biased science is only too typical an occurrence in dietary matters, as will amply appear in other connections. The Calorie approach to the problems of the dinner table is also "scientific" in origin. The vogue for oranges and grapefruit and lemons— as though the human race in America and other lands of similar climate did not live and prosper until citrus fruits came into its collective lives—is an example of a food fad

106

that started in business necessities and ended up with a tremendous outpouring of the most convincing evidence from a dozen colleges and universities. Dr. Milton Hanke's epochal and mistaken discovery that orange juice is nature's perfect remedy against tooth decay is perhaps the most sensational of all the misleading hokum that food science has given voice to in recent years, and hardly a family visitor or home demonstration agent, home-economics teacher or second-rate physician but goes about her or his daily rounds preaching God's perfect gift of citrus juices, as though oranges and the human race could not well exist apart. (The Bureau of Home Economics has lately been at work putting over iceberg lettuce in the same way that it and university laboratories some years ago helped put over oranges as a dietary necessity.) No one is so absurd as to raise the question of why, if the orange is really indispensable to health, even commercial profits can justify the destruction of huge quantities that have been harvested, in order that the selling price may be kept high on the remainder; or why, if a ripe orange is good for health, great quantities of green, *unripe* oranges are sold that have been colored to *look* ripe, by use of ethylene gas or by a dye bath applied to the skin— all this without threat of prosecution under the Food and Drug Act and indeed with the Department of Agriculture's active assistance and advice. (See Consumers' Research Bulletins of October 1933, p. 6, article "The Economics of Starvation," and of April 1935, p. 3, article "Ripe, Gassed, or Dyed Oranges?")

No one seems to think it in order to wonder why there was a higher average of adult health in an era when oranges were a treat for holidays and something hidden in a Christmas stocking than in these days when every drugstore food

counter making its special and appalling contribution to
the ill health and bad dietary of city people pours out its
gallons of "health-giving orange juice."

Some of the food fads—most, perhaps—had a partially
scientific origin; others grew out of natural errors of unscientific persons. In the first class is the vogue for raw,
uncooked foods, which is based upon some rat or guinea pig
experiments falsely generalized to human beings. The fact
that starches and proteins are digested by different organs
and processes in the stomach and intestines gave rise to the
idea that starches (e. g., cereals and potatoes) and proteins
(meat and eggs) should be eaten only at different meals.
Such dietary fads are quite unscientific, and like the vogue
for orange juice are possible of wide adoption only because
the people who adopt them are misled by a simple idea that
seems clear, understandable, and unqualified, and do not
know or are unable to follow other considerations that are
equally relevant and perhaps even more important, but take
a certain amount of critical thinking to understand and
adopt. In the case of the Hay Diet (separation of starch
and proteins at a given meal), it is forgotten that many
healthy races do mix both types of food at one meal; that
those which do not may fail to do so because one type pre-
dominates or is almost exclusively available in their dietary;
and more important still that many foods accepted everywhere as healthful and nutritious, contain both starches and
proteins in one skin (beans and peas, for example)! Even
the American Medical Association, though at times it has
contributed its share to the popularization of faddist and
unscientific dietaries among medical men and the laiety, says
editorially in its official *Journal* in criticizing the Hay Diet:
"For several generations, Americans have been eating meat

and potatoes and drinking milk, and have, as a result, produced some extraordinarily healthful [sic] and powerful human beings. Indeed nature combines proteins and carbohydrates in practically all natural food substances . . . all vegetables, fruits and cereals contain both carbohydrates and protein. A separation of proteins and carbohydrates in the diet is actually impossible, outside of a chemical laboratory, unless one chooses to subsist largely on egg white and dextrose."

One easy test of such diets as the Hay that anyone can apply without need of scientific learning is the fantastic means it uses to make its menus palatable. As the American Medical Association says, it "would torture carrots into carrot matches, splinters or horns of plenty," and "Simple mixtures of lettuce and other greens are promoted with such extraordinary titles as 'Fountain of Youth Cocktail,' 'Happy Highball,' 'Pale Moon Cocktail,' . . . 'Parcel Post Asparagus.' " It is safe for the layman to assume that anything that uses the technique used by a fourth-rate advertising agency or a newspaper "cooking school" to reach morons, is itself on a shaky or fishy basis as to its purposes or intellectual underpinning.

Another test of food fads that can be applied to many cases, but not all, is to ask: "Who stands to make money out of this?" In the case of the vogue of some years back for raisins, the supposed scientific foundation for putting it over was the idea that raisins were rich in food iron. Raisins are *not* rich in food iron, and richness in food iron is of no great importance anyway in the dietary of any people whose income is large enough to permit them to use raisins in any significant quantity. The raisin growers needed a market, and an uncritical group of home economists, egged on by clever advertising men, helped them to find it—via the iron route!

The Bureau of Home Economics and the American Home Economics Association, which on occasion print denunciations of food faddery, even more often foster food fads of the reputable type (orange juice, "alkaline" diet, raw vegetables, over-use of milk by children and adults, and so on) in their public pronouncements. Home economists and dietitians have left a long trail of dietary fads behind them and will, for lack of training in methods of scientific thought and experiment, continue to adopt and then discard faddist practices in the future. They, with their absurd emphasis on raw vegetables, baking powder biscuits as a cookery project for the high school girls, "Satisfactions Through Creative Work in Jewelry Design," [1] "Clothing inventories of women students in Teachers College," and the "Development of certain fashion magazines in the United States," [2] are in no position convincingly to attack the fads of the vitamin fanciers and the Hay Diet groups.

Prominent among the dietary fads is the "Electro-Vitamin Diet System" of Dr. Underhill, whose circular also bears the name of one Professor Hallberg, "Electrical Research Engineer," and Professor William F. Hudgings, physicist, "Exponent and Simplifier of the Einstein Theory of Relativity." This system gathers in its clients under the prepossessing institutional title of the "Philadelphia Chapter, National

[1] Title of an address at a Conference on Homemaking at Teachers College, Columbia University.

[2] These are titles of formal theses in home-economics. Other projects chosen as illustrative from official home-economics publications are: "Reactions of pre-school children to color and arrangement of food," and "The history of table manners and customs and the influence upon manners and customs of South Louisiana."

Health Conservation." In Los Angeles there is a cult with the high-sounding title Food Chemistry Educational Institute, which publishes its "Food Science" journal, one issue of which boosts the wonderful system of Dr. Kolar, "Bloodless Surgery." This organization also runs a school of Scientific Feeding. But from these to the elaborate array of Calorie and acid-base equilibrium calculations of Dr. Mary Swartz Rose of Columbia University or Dr. E. V. McCollum of Johns Hopkins, and the enlarged use of green leafy vegetables urged by the government's Bureau of Home Economics, is not so far a cry as the "scientific nutritionists" would have one believe.

Lest these aspersions on the food and diet cults seem based too much on general charges, we may examine briefly some of the assertions made, though it is noteworthy that the printed literature of the organizations is often of a come-on nature, designed to lure one into a course of correspondence school lessons or a course of personal instruction under a great leader of nutritional notions and novelties. The Food Chemistry Educational Institute modestly adopts a program that includes reform of capitalism via the food supply ("to go into business for the people of the U. S. A. instead of for ourselves") and the elimination of the criminal population by correction of their Health. Its special surgical and dietary novelties include: Dr. Kolar, the Bloodless Surgeon, "Organic Mineral Broth Powder," W. H. Y. ("used in place of coffee or tea"), Slender Sweets (Slenderize the Movie Star Way). No one, to our knowledge, had ever alleged that movie stars had gone "into business for the people of the U. S. A." instead of for themselves.

The Electro-Vitamin Diet System is simpler; one needs Phosphorus to correct "failing intellectual powers"; "the

forgetful need manganese; a leathery, old-looking skin calls
for fluorine; if iodine and magnesium are deficient acid may
invade the brain resulting in melancholia"; and so on ad
nauseam. This system appeals, no doubt wisely, to the same
group who give ear to the demagogies of the Hearst newspapers, namely, "people who think"—or as the Electro-
Vitamin people put it, but with less generality than Mr.
Hearst, "executives, clergymen, lawyers, teachers and other
professional people."

The ingenuity of the Electro-Vitamin Diet exploiters is
considerable; if you exhibit a scientific approach to your
dietetic problems and consult a physician for your troubles,
you can at the same time be so unscientific as to go right on
with Electro-Vitamin Diet treatment, which "will aid you
in making selections and combinations in harmony with his
[the physician's] plans." The unscientific nature of the assertions about iodine, manganese, and fluorine, hardly call
for explicit refutation to anyone who is likely to be even
interested in a rational approach to the problem of diet.
Suffice it to say that this is one of the oldest and most
ridiculous of all the diet quackeries, and that its harmful
effect will in fact be pretty well limited to the very "people
who think" and adopt the curious practice of reading the
yellow journals and the tabloids, and hearkening to radio
announcers as their peculiar mode of demonstrating it. The
Electro-Vitamin Diet System has one other feature that
shows its kinship with yellow journalism's newspapers and
magazines. Being a diet cult, it carefully dissociates itself
from the diet cults by saying, "This Diet System replaces
diet fads with a real science of nutrition. . . ." Much as
Mr. Hearst, the friend of Hitler, of demagogy, and of vul-
gar, concentrated, irresponsible and oppressive wealth,

adopts, when in the presence of the mob, his pleasing coloration of the true patriot and the friend of the worker, the lowly and downtrodden.

The dietary cults and quackeries are too numerous to list in any degree of detail. New ones are born almost daily, while others thrive for a time and reappear under a new name and often with a new line of hokum. A few of the dietary cults that have come to the attention of Consumers' Research are the two named above, and the following: Defensive-Diet League of America, Toledo, Ohio, which lists both dentists and physicians on its literature, its special line being:

[A picture of a balance]
20%   80%
Acid   Alkalin
The Weigh to Health

"Associate" membership and dues for one year come to $16; the Cook Book is $7.50; Dietary Advice by mail, $2 per letter; or $10 per year and up; Bulletins only, Annual Subscription, $3.50. Its membership is also made up of people who think—"of clear thinking, intelligent men and women." (It almost seems to be the rule that if the appeal is to the especially gullible, you should make some reference to the "people who think"!) Among the physicians connected with the Defensive-Diet League were, at one time, an "Original Milk and Rest Cure" devotee; another doctor, W. H. Hay of Buffalo, also a rest cure operator; and one Oscar Jones, a cancer cure man ("my cure is guaranteed").

Another food fad organization is Basic Brands Laboratory (Los Angeles and Toledo), which has a line of *Sea Vita* (Health from the Sea):

Sea Vita with added Iron (Formula AFE)

Sea Vita with added Calcium (Formula ACA)

Sea Vita with added Sodium (Formula ASA)

Sea Vita with added Manganese (Formula APM)

Sea Vita with added Desert Herbs (Formula ADS)

Sea Vita Kelp

Sea Vita White Sea Lettuce, and finest grades of
    Peppermint Leaves.

A Dr. C. O. B. writes of *Sea Vita* tablets, according to
the *Sea Vita* literature: "Calm, peaceful sleep at night and
every night. . . . Not one fit of the 'blues' in the ten days;
glory be for that. A sense of elation; a desire to be doing
something all the time." It is impossible to comment adequately on Dr. C. O. B.'s findings without knowing what
it was that he desired to be doing at all times.

It is impossible to give more space in this book to the
discussion of cultist food and health agencies—but their
characteristics show a singular uniformity in their dependence upon certain ideas that to a layman without scientific
training sound impressively scientific and to the scientist
(Electrical Engineer Hallberg and Physicist Hudgings to
the contrary notwithstanding) are easily recognized as the
sheerest nonsense. Food quackeries rely mainly upon such
ideas or nostrum-products as fasting, "mineral" broths and
concentrates, raw fruits and vegetables, "natural" foods
(meaning in this case, natural foods sold by a particular
exploiter or by a "Health Food Shoppe"), milk feeding,
acidophilus milk or cultured buttermilk feeding, orange juice
feeding; dietaries limited to a few items, such as the Hollywood diet of grapefruit and lamb chops, or the milk and
whole wheat diet; roughage feeding (the breakfast food,
bran, spinach, and lettuce cult); the vegetarian and fruitar-

ian diet that condemns as putrefactive and stultifying and corruptive of brain and body energy a diet that includes meat and eggs; the vitamin cult that wraps up all health values in a package of vitamin concentrates and "special vitamin foods"; and the mineral cults, of which one has already been discussed, that distinguish food values on the basis of the content of iron, chlorine, fluorine, iodine, and so on. Especially bad for children, and dietetically and economically pointless as well, is the growing and very expensive puréed-canned-spinach cult, the main result of which has been to distort children's diet to the enrichment of can manufacturers and a special group of canners of a very high-priced product.

One more word about food faddery: There seems to be something about novel and unscientific ideas on eating which appeals especially to radicals and liberals. There may be something at least in the view that radicalism is associated to a degree with digestive discomfort and undernourishment. It is certain that radicals and liberals like Debs and Upton Sinclair have fallen for some of the most atrocious nonsense on diet and health that has ever been concocted. Whole colonies of political liberals and some exceptionally "Christian" people in Y. M. C. A.'s and welfare organizations go in for diets predominating in cereals, raw vegetables, and nuts; eschew coffee because it is popular, and drink cocoa because it isn't—not knowing that dietetically coffee without cream and sugar is the less harmful of the two beverages. To these people I should like to say that the New Society will not necessarily involve new food ideas; it may find it wise to go back to many *old* food ideas. In point of fact, it will be extremely radical, from the standpoint of big business and its partners in plunder, the state and federal governments, to give up the new and return to the old and well-tested, wholesome, unadulterated, and unsophisticated in foods and drink. In time to come, the man who insists on unsprayed apples and unsulphured dried apricots is sure to be scorned as a consumer-red and loudly commanded to go back where he came from if he protests American sulphur and American arsenic.

Unfortunately for the simplicity of the analogies, the rottenness of capitalism's abuses is in no wise paralleled by any sound doctrine that meat rots in the intestines. The radical needs to use his mind and his eyes more; is not the man-eating tiger a healthy fellow, and does *he* eat raw cabbages and carrots and huckleberries with sour cream? Was not man a hunting, raw-meat-eating animal long before he was a browser in libraries and in vegetarian Health Cafeterias full of potassium broth, sour cream, and Vitamin F Salad?

The saddest of all human beings is the man who, unhappy about the future of mankind, as he is well-justified in being, increases his own special and individual irritation and unhappiness by eating, at an increased price above the normal diet, "health food" and acidophilus milk and raw dates and bran, and so exacerbates his stomach ulcer and further wounds his colicky intestines! "Health food" has about the same relation to health that the glaring, smelly ultra-violet lamp used in a New York apartment, a Turkish bath or a Y. M. C. A. gymnasium has to a sunny, balsam-laden, summer day on breeze-swept Blue Mountain Lake in the Adirondacks.

The subject of fad foods is, of course, a branch of that of food fads—and what one says about undesirable and unscientific eating practices in general is easily extended to include specific food articles often recommended as priceless boons to hungry or suffering humanity. A short list by brand name of some of these food nostrums or habitually or commonly misrepresented articles is presented below. A few of these are discussed in detail elsewhere, and the list below is in any case to be regarded as merely suggestive, and is to be understood and interpreted in the light of information and points of view to be found elsewhere in this book.

FOOD AND BEVERAGE NOSTRUMS WITH QUOTATIONS FROM CLAIMS MADE FOR THE PRODUCTS

MATE [1]

Congoin ...."Notice when you start out for a day's work after several cups of Congoin the spring in your step and how easily your lungs take in the fresh air. . . . Notice in the evening when listening to the radio, what a complete power of relaxation Congoin gives. . . ."

Joyz Maté ...."If you do not feel up to par, if you want to feel above the average switch to Joyz."

[1] The leaves of a South American herb called "yerba maté." This herb has caffeine and tannin as its active ingredients; consequently its nutritive and blood-building effects are simply those of tea or coffee, that is, practically nothing. The claims made for the nutritive qualities of such beverages are absurd. The element "chlorophyl" is found in all green leaves (mint, for example, or water cress, or parsley, or tea), a fact which deprives of any significance the supposed uniqueness of maté in this respect. The advertising of maté has been ingenious in its use of pseudo-scientific appeals and endorsements of eminent experts from far-off South American countries. Science in South America, as in North, often has its very reasonable price. (From Consumers' Research, Inc., *Special Bulletin 20*, May, 1935, by special permission.)

Juno Maté .... "It is a tonic, stimulant, digestive and diuretic. Physiologists and hygienists recommend it for its remarkable nourishing qualities."

Maté Del Morro .... "After taking Maté Del Morro the mouth has a fresh, clean taste and the breath is pure and sweet."

Nova Maté .... "This noble and privileged plant possesses many beneficial qualities."

Virile Maté .... ". . . ideal as a tonic and stimulant, but it helps to reduce excess weight caused by starchy foods, by ridding the body of its acid accumulations."

Viton Maté .... "You can laugh at old age and all its attendant ills—if you use Viton Maté."

MINERAL FOODS

Alberty's Products:

Alberty's Food, Instant ⎱ CALCIUM the staff of life . . .
Alberty's Food, Regular ⎰ Alberty's food . . . rebuilds the intestinal tract and is the only food yet discovered that does.

Organic Food Pellets ...

Availaform Kelp .... "Improved function of the important THYROID GLAND . . . is ONE exceedingly probable, advantageous result of its use."

Calaqua .... "CALAQUA . . . helps any ailment for the better because it makes your blood stream alkaline!"

Io-Food Products:

Io-Food .... "A safe stable one-half percent organic iodine solution."

Io-Sol .... Said to be, "a 5% organic iodine food addition, for the enrichment of bread, pastry, and milk."

Iokelp .... "Eating demineralized and devitalized foods year after year, as most of us do, produces a condition that is very difficult to overcome but which *Iokelp* tablets can often correct in time. *Iokelp* made from fresh kelp, highly concentrated, contains liberal quantities of iodine, iron, copper and other minerals absolutely essential for bodily health."

Kelp-A-Malt .... "Regain lost pep and youthful energy this easy scientific way." "Natural Assimilable Iodine . . . Kelpamalt's the greatest weight and strength builder there is. . . ."

Kelpe'koe .... "KELPE'KOE, *Tea of the Sea,* is more than a medicine, it is a health building and maintenance tonic, one that provides the sixteen mineral salts necessary for the well being of the human body. . . . It contains nothing other than that which was placed in it by Nature. Following is a list of the mineral elements found in the *Tea of the Sea:* calcium, phosphorus, potassium, sulphur, sodium, chlorine, magnesium, iron, silicon, iodine, manganese, aluminum, copper, lithium, nickel, and cobalt."

Kelpodine .... "*Kelpodine* supplies not only amply [sic] iodine requirements but is rich in all other essential minerals that are so frequently lacking in the daily bill of fare."

Par 16 Bread .... "Keep up to par with Par 16"

Paracelsus .... "Fine testimonials from aged folks."

Potassium Broth .... A powder made of a combination of vegetables that is supposed to impart to the system the most potassium.

Vegetrate .... "Vegetrates . . . reduce the secretion of acids . . . aid in neutralizing the acids which are already there."

MINERALS AND VITAMINS

Anabolic Food No. 4 ..... "This food is a scientific combination of Spinach, Celery, Horseradish, Endive, and Lettuce."

Availaform Vegetables

Burbank Vegetable Tablets "Each . . . Tablet . . . can be considered equal to more than one pound of fresh green leafy vegetables. . . ."

Kelvita .... "KNOW THE THRILL OF BEING FULLY ALIVE—THE JOY OF VIBRANT ENERGY."

Parkelp .... "Our vegetables and fruit as well as bread and meats, no longer supply sufficient food minerals."

Vitamineralis .... "After taking Vitamineralis a short time, you will begin to regain your youthful appearance . . . if weak or run down, your health and vitality will commence to improve . . . you'll be able to think better and produce more."

VITAMIN FOODS

Catalyn .... "Because of its highly concentrated vitamin content, Catalyn has the remarkable property of promoting vitality, even when taken in very small amounts."

Malt-O-Egg .... ". . . we use . . . pure cane sugar . . . full cream dry milk . . . high quality malted milk. . . ."

Vita-Co .... "A meal in a teaspoon."

Vitamin Candy Bars ..... "*Vitamin* A-B-C-D-E-G Energy Bar. . . . *Vitamin* Candy Bars are Chock-full of the Following Health Building Properties: Vitamins . . . Minerals . . . Carbohydrates . . . Proteins . . . Fats . . . Phosphates and Sterols . . ."

SPECIAL AND MISCELLANEOUS FOOD NOSTRUMS

Alvita Tablets

Battle Creek Products:

B-Lac .... "The new health sugar to supplement the use of Lacto Dextrin and to be used to keep the flora in a healthy condition."

Bran biscuits .... "Bulk supplying."

Branola .... "Foods for well folks to keep them well."

Fatless spread .... "Reducing food."

Fig bromose ....⎫
Nut bromose ....⎬ "Fattening foods."

Food Ferrin, sweetened. "(86 calories per ounce) One of the most important foods for the underweight. Highly concentrated food iron. Builds up bodily resistance to disease. Also fattening, because Meltose Honey forms the base of this renowned Battle Creek food." [Food Ferrin is also in unsweetened form for diabetics.]

Lacto Dextrin .... "Purpose—To change the intestinal flora and combat the poisons which cripple the colon. . . . It is a scientific preparation of lactose and dextrin, flavored with lemon, provided in the form of a pulverized sugar, and is served as a delicious and easy-to-take beverage."

Laxa biscuit .... "A crisp, crunchy biscuit of Bran and Agar, rich in phosphates and Vitamin B. Excellent for providing the bulk needed to promote elimination."

Meltose Honey .... "(86 calories per ounce) An excellent source of iron and lime made from grains and easily assimilated. A delicious spread for bread, when mixed with a little soft butter, or with cream."

No-Fat (mayonnaise) .. "Reducing food."

Nuttolene .... "A pure nut product having the consistency of cream cheese. Excellent for stews, sandwiches, and salads."

Protose .... "Looks, smells, and tastes like meat, but is made from wheat gluten and nuts to provide protein and iron."

Savita .... "Purely vegetable and nonfattening. Its meatlike flavor appeases the craving for meats; it is rich in the *Vitamin B Complex* and contains valuable iron for blood building. . . . Available in paste form, salt, and bouillon cubes."

Vita Wheat . . . . "A very easily digested cereal. . . . Fattening foods. . . . Foods for acid stomach."

ZO . . . . "A dextrinized cereal, which, softened with hot water and served with cream, is a safe nutrient in cases of hyperacidity. ZO supplies ten times as much iron as ordinary bread; four times as much as beefsteak; and three times as much as spinach. . . . ZO is rich in iron and lime, also in Vitamin B."

ZO Flakes . . . . "Foods for well folks to keep them well."

Dietene . . . . "It embodies all the reducing diet principles used by the nutritional experts in the professional field."

Dr. Jackson's Foods:

Bekus Puddy . . . . "Alkaline. . . . Has a benign effect upon the kidneys."

Dr. Jackson Meal . . . . . "After only three packages you will note a marked improvement in your sense of physical and mental resilience and well-being."

Lishus . . . . "Lishus is designed especially as a food for weak and irritated digestive organs; for ulceration and colitis; the aged, ailing and convalescent. . . ."

Little Crow Coco-Wheats.. "Coco-Wheats supplies vital energy quickly and easily without burdening digestion."

Manikin Tea .... "Manikin . . . For a Fashionable Figure Guaranteed Absolutely Safe. . . . Slim, graceful figure. . . . Have one yourself. . . . Effectively promotes Chemical Balance. . . . To attain a youthful athletic figure. . . . The Sylphlike Figure of a Fashion Manikin. . . . Have One Yourself."

Miel-de Maguey
Nutro .... " . . . healthier than meat for it contains no poisonous bacteria; no uric acid; no ptomaine poison."

Seavigor .... "If you want new youthful vitality . . . if you want lots of stamina, vigorous manhood, boundless energy and endurance, then use *Seavigor*."

Dr. Stoll's Diet Aid ...... " 'Dr. Stoll's Diet-Aid' . . . was labeled to give the impression that it could be used as a substitute for certain meals, and that such use would cause loss of weight. Food and Drug officials analyzed the 'Diet Aid,' and found that it . . . consisted essentially of corn starch, sugar, cacao powder, and caramel."

Syl-Wey .... "Syl-Wey is unique in the combination of its ingredients and its value in malfunction of the digestive tract is enhanced by the fact that it is ingested in the nature of a food, promoting bowel activity by furnish-

ing Bulk and Lubrication Without
Irritation."

Taro-Mano ....". . . most admirably effective in
all stomach and intestinal disorders
and of unexcelled dietetic merit, due
to non-existence of acidity."

Vegecandy
Veg-Malted
Vitrofa

QUACK HEALTH ENTERPRISES

(Two examples out of scores that might be given.)

East Aurora Sun and Diet Sanitorium—Dr. William H. Hay,
of Hay Diet fame, is medical director. Both Dr. Hay and the
Aurora Sun and Diet Sanitorium have been fully exposed in
the *Journal of the American Medical Association,* Bureau of
Investigation, Feb. 25, 1935.

Dr. Floyd James Carter, D.C., Ph.C., terms himself a
"radionic specialist" and according to his letterhead is a "representative for the Hay system of diet." Dr. Carter diagnoses
ailments by use of the " 'Radioclast' which actually 'tunes in'
on the vibrations of the body and registers instantly all
abnormalities."

VIII

DIET FADS OF THE UPPER CLASSES

Many whose conduct in the kitchen and at the table is determined in very high degree by faddist and cultist dietary teachings, regard themselves as quite above that class of persons who get their food information uncritically from radio announcers and the *Ladies' Home Journal* kitchenette-chefs and its home-economics concoctors of salads of canned figs and grapes stuffed with a mixture of cream and Roquefort cheese. Unfortunately, the average man or woman of the comfortable middle classes is just as badly bound up in imposed habit patterns of food preparation and selection as is any ignoramus who has fallen for the latest Hollywood "slimming diet," potassium broth or a regimen of "purifying fruit juices." The half-starved, less-than-half educated bank clerk or college instructor who stands in front of a "pure-food restaurant" window to watch the pressing of spinach juice, carrot juice, and turnip juice from the raw vegetables, has his exact sociological counterpart in the college-trained bond salesman or advertisement writer who sits at breakfast in the University Club or the Women's City Club eating a meal of orange or grapefruit juice, puffed wheat with rich cream, and coffee. Of this meal the plan and pattern have been laid down almost as directly by the business-like gentlemen and ladies who run the home-economics departments of the California Fruit Growers Association, the national packaged-food distributors and the swell kitchens of the *Delineator* and *Good Housekeeping Institute,* as though these single-minded folk were standing beside the breakfast table dictating a list of the items to be eaten. It is hard to imagine an upper class breakfast being served anywhere in these days without its copious serving of orange juice, a vogue which runs all the way from the stock broker's yacht, to the slender glass before the stenographer of the Fourth National Bank of Binghamton, who is picking up a hasty sip and bite at the drug store on the corner on her way to punch the office time clock, a minute and a half before nine. Yet the orange juice craze is a dietary fad and nothing but a fad. It has brought untold millions of dollars to Florida and California business men, to advertising agents and to the women's magazines, and has reconditioned millions of otherwise intelligent Americans to the belief, as stoutly held in effect as it is false, that raw fruit juices are as essential to life as milk to the babe, or water to us all.

Just why intelligent adults should be so incapable of examining the assumptions underlying their choice of food as to think that the human race must have been cradled in an orange grove, and could not have lived properly any farther away from such a grove than the fastest camels and oxen could rush the golden fruit, is beyond the power of this author to explain. Anthropologists (though they also follow the citrus fruit fad) could tell you just how wrong ideas and pseudo-scientific notions spread through primitive people, usually at a very slow rate except where compelling economic necessity is involved. Nevertheless none has examined the primitive reactions and responses to repeated stimuli of supposedly civilized and educated people when confronted by a sufficient number of billboards showing oranges being squeezed into glasses; by enough home-

economics teachers talking pseudo-science, taught them in
turn by nutrition teachers whose special technical skills were
acquired by animal experimentation on a very limited class
of animals, almost invariably rodents (rats and guinea
pigs) ; and finally and most importantly by a sufficient number of advertisements and news stories printed in every
newspaper and every popular magazine. The "educational"
advertisements and stories are based upon the assumption,
if the matter is analyzed, that oranges (or canned tomato
juice) and healthy infants and adults have gone together
at all times and all places, and that people who try to live
without these particular food substances are like people living in a fog or in the Kansas Bible Belt, quite unable to
reach the fullness of their being.

Fortunately for the race, there are some things that pass
as science that can be tested by anyone. It is quite beyond
the capacity of a person of general education and average
intelligence to subject to satisfactory and convincing proof
or disproof the doctrine that the refrigerant gas used in a
certain widely sold electrical refrigerator impinging on a gas
flame of a kitchen gas stove, may give rise to a deadly war-
gas, phosgene, but anyone above the age of 12 can check on
the theory behind the citrus fruit fad or the milk-for-adults
fad, or the bicarbonate of soda and milk of magnesia fads,
or the canned pineapple fad, the bran fad, or the spinach
cult, for himself. One test of a scientific theory is that if it
directly conflicts with the known facts at any point, it is
invalid, and the only limitation upon this test is that the
known facts with which it seems to be in conflict must be
genuine, verifiable facts and not themselves a theory. If
it is a fact, and indeed it is, that wide and great consumption of orange juice is a new phenomenon in the world and

one pretty generally limited to Americans, and that up until
the last ten years or so the race flourished and reproduced
well without the pouring out of rivers of orange, lemon and
grapefruit juice, and if it be true, as it is true, that orange
growers and advertising men and women's magazines and
newspapers, and university teachers of home-economics and
radio stations in certain states had a big stake in selling and
helping to sell oranges and orange products and in making
oranges into a household necessity like eggs or flour, it requires no further reasoning whatever to dispose of the
orange, lemon, and grapefruit juice problem. Since the race
lived well, and in some regions especially well, without either
oranges, advertising or home-economics, and lived well in
thousands of places where oranges do not grow and to which
they are not brought, it is a matter requiring only a high
school boy's reasoning to see that citrus fruit, like *Listerine*,
may be merely something novel in our culture; by this reasoning citrus fruit has no necessary or significant place
whatever in our dietary (which is not properly a transient
thing of advertising and home-economics teaching at all, but
a matter of science *and* culture). The loss of the citrus fruit
fad, however, will be a tremendous blow when it comes to
the learned doctors of California and Columbia and Chicago
universities, to *Good Housekeeping Institute* and to the
U. S. Bureau of Home Economics. (Even the latter after
all has a great duty to California and Florida, since the
Bureau's admitted function, and a function very recently
insisted upon by Congress, is to help *sell* farm products, not
to tell the unvarnished truth about them.) Fortunately for
these people, there is always in a profit society something
or some one else to whom the masses can be sold when one
of the rackets has played out. Cod-liver oil, also almost a

food specialty now to America's millions, has served well; Iceberg lettuce is one of the newest saviours of the race discovered by the Federal Bureau of Home Economics for the benefit of lettuce growers in the Imperial Valley; raw carrots and cabbage are coming in though they suffer from the grave disadvantage that there is no big business interest as there was with citrus fruit, to be helped financially at the cost of the whole population. Milk has been in tremendous vogue for nearly twenty years, and untold harm has been done to human stomachs that were never meant to consume milk after babyhood, merely because no very simple and very outlandish scientist has arisen until recently to point out the fact that everyone knew already, did he but use his head, that milk was the appropriate and scientifically adapted food only of the very young animal of mammalian species. A little fact like that packs enough dynamite in itself to blow most of the Borden, Walker-Gordon, and Sheffield and ice cream manufacturers' advertising to kingdom come, but somebody has to say it and millions have to repeat it before anything can happen that need bother the Borden interests. It may be that the extremely high salaries paid to presidents of milk companies is in part a compensation for having that dividend-centered type of mind that would not go off chasing such disturbing ideas in the public interest as the one that, given a good, native, unspoiled, and uncommercialized diet, only young children and some few adults under medical care require milk in significant amounts in their diet.

To revert to the problem of oranges, grapefruit and lemons, there is hardly any adult living today who cannot remember when oranges were principally an ornament and a delicacy, often destined for the Christmas stocking or as a birthday present; when lemons were for flavor, like vanilla, and very occasionally for lemonade; and when grapefruit, if known at all, was a curiosity and a very unpromising one.

And now again, through the ingenious devices of the professional food adulterators and their chemical and bio-chemical hirelings, citrus fruits are being restored in this country to their original status as Christmas tree and restaurant window ornaments, rather than something which is fit and wholesome to eat. Senator Royal S. Copeland is well known as an employe of patent medicine interests and a frequent broadcaster for commercial enterprise, and as one who has not been inclined to exaggerate in favor of consumers, yet it was he who used the apt phrase "painted humbugs" in describing oranges now on the market. Interposing a remark in the course of the testimony of an apple grower at the recent hearings on his Food and Drug Bill, Senator Copeland said: "We do know that there are oranges sold, which are not oranges in their right sense. They are painted humbugs."

Of late, there have appeared on the market great quantities of oranges stamped "Color Added." (It was to these that the Senator referred in particular.) The following conversation was overheard recently in a Chicago grocery store.

Customer: "What does 'Color Added' on these oranges mean?"

Store manager: "That's just the trade name, madam. It doesn't mean anything."

After all, many a trade name, especially in connection with food products, is nothing more than a designation for a "humbug," and the manager of the store was nearer right than he realized in saying "It doesn't mean anything."

As with the paint manufacturers whose slogan is, "Save the surface and you save all," the orange growers hold to the view that if you color the skin, you "ripen" the whole orange.

The conventional manner used by the orange-cosmeticians of treating oranges is still the use of ethylene gas. When this method of faking oranges to make unripe ones appear ripe is used, there is no government regulation requiring that its use be disclosed by a label on the orange as is required when dye is added. On the contrary, the practice of this humbuggery, or orange faking if you will, has the full endorsement of Secretary Wallace. In a Department of Agricultural protocol issued over the Secretary's name, it is held by an amazing legalism of the type which comes to its fullest flower in government bureaus, that the ethylene treatment simply "unmasks" the ripe yellow color which Nature, if given some weeks more in which to do its work for consumers, would have put upon the oranges. The same reasoning as that used by the government is that of the hair dye manufacturers who hold that their particular hair dye does not color the hair, but merely permits nature to "restore" the original shade. It is but a short step from this reasoning to the view that when Farmer Green paints his barn, he is but "unmasking" the original red color of the lumber, and that an overdose of green apples merely unmasks the stomach ache which little Willie has already.

There are two reasons back of this monkey-business in oranges. First, it is done to enable the growers, at considerably less expense to themselves, to place green fruit with its better keeping qualities in distant markets and at an earlier date when market demand and prices are at their maximum. Second, it is one more item in the long list of practices known as increasing "eye appeal," without regard to taste and stomach appeal. Let us hope that some day a compilation will be made of all of the numerous methods and practices legitimatized by the government service by which a third or fourth rate product (such as butter produced from stall-fed cows eating dry fodder and cottonseed meal) is made to resemble exactly the finest product of cows pastured under the most perfect conditions, in meadows of succulent green grass and clover.

In their complete disregard for the intelligence of consumers, orange growers also practice other tricks as well as "unmasking" ripeness. A borax bath is often given to increase the keeping qualities of the oranges; and a coating of paraffin adds a shine to the exterior, which it is hoped will make a sufficiently strong psychological impression upon the eater to cause him to forget the disagreeably sour and unripe taste of the fruit itself. Government standards in nearly all foodstuffs, it should be noted, are set primarily with reference to these outer and non-essential qualities and appearances. U. S. "Fancy" must be well colored. If it is only slightly colored it drops to the lowest grade, even though, as Mr. Wallace puts it, it is really ripe and needs only to have its color "unmasked."

In Florida, the liberal use of lead and arsenic sprays on citrus fruits in order to bring them earlier to maturity—i.e., a kind of maturity which makes them saleable a few weeks sooner—is common, and has recently been legalized by a decision of the Supreme Court in that State. This decision overturned a law that had sought to prevent the treating of citrus fruits by the poison-spray for the protection of the consumer and to maintain fair competition among growers.

In contrast with the strong anti-consumer bias of the Department of Agriculture of the United States, an official

publication of the Australian government emphatically denounces all of this humbuggery in the marketing of fruits.
It warns the consumers of that country that the great bulk
of citrus fruits is being made to appear ripe by the treatment with ethylene gas. (In Australia exhaust gases containing ethylene from motor car engines are or were used.)
"After such treatment," the official publication declares,
"the green, sour, unripe oranges are still sour, unripe
oranges, despite their golden yellow skin; the green, hard,
unripe bananas are still hard, unripe bananas despite their
attractive artificial yellow skin; and the green, sour, unripe
pineapples are still sour, unripe pineapples despite the de-
ceitful yellow colour of the skin. There is no question that
in such cases the practice is fraudulent, as it is done solely
with intent to give unripe fruit the appearance of being ripe,
and so to deceive the buyers." Just why government and science in the United States should be so unreservedly and inevitably on the side of financial interests and against consumers is a nice question. Foreigners are often puzzled to
know why the action of the officials, which is normally expected in protection of the consumer population in foreign
countries, is not taken in the United States under exactly
the same circumstances. Some of my readers may wish to
ask Mr. Wallace and Mr. Roosevelt why it is that in Australia the green, sour, unripe oranges are still sour, unripe
oranges after the ethylene treatment, but in America the
same treatment results merely in "unmasking" the ripe yellow color of the mature fruit which Nature, in her carelessness, has failed to provide—in time for the January ship-
ping season.

The tremendously touted vitamin C which citrus fruits
contain and of which the human race is supposed—by the

orange industry—to require huge quantities, is one that the rat, the principal laboratory animal (upon whose life and responses to food most food research depends) seems not to require at all. The guinea pig, also an experimental animal, *does* require vitamin C and unfortunately for mankind, happens also to be the animal—cheap, and easily standardized, and quickly reproduced—much used for experimental work on foods, though the guinea pig is a native of the tropics and hence has had access during the period of his evolution, to a very different type of food supply than that consumed by small rodent animals in the American climate and geography. The guinea pig is also one of those very exceptional animals which must get his vitamin C directly in his diet, because he is unable to produce it in his own body as do dogs, cats, and fowl and other animals of our climate.

It was from the vegetarian guinea pig's reactions to deprivation of this vitamin that the interesting and well-exploited scientific exaggeration of the importance of raw fruits and vegetables for their content of vitamin C grew up; and this alone created the foundation of the tremendous citrus industry and in a very real and practical sense a large share of the profitable business of running women's magazines and home-economics columns in newspapers. In spite of this elaborate exploitation of the C vitamin, little is known as to the quantity of the vitamin needed, or its possible relation to the other factors in the food intake (such as the proportions of protein or carbohydrate foods used) characteristic of the guinea pig as compared with other animals or with man. It is well established for example that although the rabbit is of the same family as the guinea pig, his nutritional requirement with respect to vitamin C differs markedly from the guinea pig's—if indeed the rabbit requires any vitamin C at all.

Magazine editors can't write food articles around roast beef (unless it's canned), broiled fish, plain wheaten bread, baked potatoes, apple sauce, and well-aged native cheese, and at the same time provide a sufficient diversity of adjectives and natural color photographs for alluring advertising; it is absolutely necessary to bring in things that are or can advantageously be advertised, which means packaged or effectively identified (*Sunkist*, for example, or *Blue Goose*). And so far as the home-economists are concerned, if they do most of their reading in the same kind of journals as the untrained housewife and rely upon jobs or money and material subsidies for research from the food manufacturers who have packaged and identified products to sell, their notably tame and conventional minds can be relied upon to fall in line in every way that could be desired by the president of the California fruit association or of General Mills or General Foods or Borden's.

Oranges are especially in vogue just now in university and *Good Housekeeping* circles as a means of preventing tooth decay (which, incidentally, *isn't* being prevented but is actually getting worse, the higher the rivers of orange juice and of various synthetic vitamin preparations flow). A street car advertisement of Sunkist Oranges says: "*Insure Sound, Healthy Teeth and Gums*. Science prescribes two 8 ounce glasses daily of fresh orange juice with the juice of half a lemon in each." But orange juice is in fact not a cure for acidosis nor a preventive of falling hair or decaying teeth. Science does *not* prescribe two 8 ounce glasses of orange and lemon juice daily. But $cience undoubtedly does! And thousands of dentists have believed this pseudo-science instead of following their own good common sense, which should be able to think back, except in the case of very young dentists, to the days before orange juice and viosterol and Sunshine-vitamin Bread.

As Dr. Weston A. Price said recently in the *Journal of the American Dental Association*, many of those who are immune to tooth decay "in both the high Alpine valleys and the interior of the Isle of Lewis have probably never eaten an orange or grapefruit and in neither district were wild berries [nutritionally similar to citrus fruit] provided as a native food. Some citrus fruits come into Switzerland from Italy and Spain, but they reach only communities provided with adequate means of transportation. No district was found with immunity [to tooth decay] where imported fruits were available. This would seem at once to exclude the possibility of vitamin C being a controlling factor in these districts."

Indeed, the latest researches by a dentist, not a rat-and-guinea-pig nutrition laboratorian, shows of a certainty that excessive use of orange and lemon juice causes *destruction* of teeth by decalcification. Dr. Samuel Charles Miller, head of New York University's peridontia department, finds teeth destroyed not only by hard candies, which he found singularly destructive of tooth enamel, but by citrus fruit juices. Lozenges, cough drops, and throat tablets, commonly dissolved slowly in the mouth, were found by constant use to play havoc with the teeth—to the extent, in the case of one woman, of 21 cavities produced in a six months' period.

It would be hard to cite a better case of the dangers of food faddism than this effective debunking of the orange-juice mania. The devotee consumes endless quantities of oranges to get the vitamin C which the nutritionists (studying guinea pigs) assure him will preserve his (not guinea pigs') teeth and prevent their decay; the citric and other fruit acids contained in the oranges, ruin the teeth the vitamin C was found (in guinea pigs) to preserve. If there were good teeth in your family some generations back, you may be *sure* that they were not the result either of the advertising of the product of the California fruit association or of the "scientists" who so tremendously tout orange and lemon juice for them.

Evidently these great Florida and California sources of vitamin C are a little less necessary than Dr. Hanke, Dr. Eddy of *Good Housekeeping,* and the orange growers would have us believe.

As already noted, the book *Diet and Dental Health,* by Milton T. Hanke is mainly a big, helpful boost for the citrus fruit industry. The experiment on 440 children at "Mooseheart" which is reported on in this book and which is supposed to show that the consumption of a pint of orange juice a day will arrest dental caries (tooth decay) in many cases, was paid for by the California Fruit Growers' Exchange. The *Journal of the American Medical Association* had an extensive review of the book showing how completely unscientific it is. Dr. Hanke has also been of service to the Western Company, manufacturers of *Dr. West's* Tooth Paste, when he "initiated on his own volition an investigation into the characteristics of the leading dentifrices on the market," and arrived at conclusions regarding the superabundant merits of this particular toothpaste, that suggest advertising more than they do the work of a scientific investigator.

Vitamin C is not, as a matter of fact, one of the vitamins

that is low in the American diet of the well-fed classes; anyone could figure that out for himself who remembered the blooming health of his Aunt Emma when she was a young woman far from the orange groves and blissfully unaware even of their future whereabouts. If you do not remember Aunt Emma clearly enough to be sure, turn for a moment to the old red-plush-covered photo album in your attic and see if those healthy and hearty solid-food-eating ancestors and uncles of yours really looked the mangy and unhappy way a guinea pig in the pictures in the physiology book does, after he has been deprived of his daily meal of orange juice.

Just how far the orange insanity can go, may best be exemplified by an article of W. A. McKeever, A.M., Ph.M., LL.D., condensed from *Health Culture* for the *Health Digest* of May, 1935. Dr. McKeever helps his readers "outwit the stimulant habit" by directing them to alkalinize the blood stream by subsisting entirely for two weeks or more on fruits and vegetables, cream and honey, which he evidently thinks were and are the common, natural foods of primitive man, as decidedly they were and are not. He wants his readers to give up meat, fish, and fowl, which were and are the predominantly natural food of primitive man who can get them. "You could live and thrive," he says, "for a month on nothing but oranges eating both pulp and juice, if you should take about 16 to 24 of them per day, and lose almost no weight. You are especially requested to eat liberally of oranges, pulp and all, during this restorative period. Eat them at rising time, bed time, mid-forenoon, mid-afternoon, if convenient. An occasional alternative will be grapefruit unsweetened or pure pineapple juice, or tomato juice, or grape juice, all unsweetened. You may mix a bit of one of these fruit juices with your fruit-cream-honey meals, if you wish."

But we must go on and see what is claimed for this amazing fruit-honey-cream quackery. After one has read this, one ceases to wonder why there are so many sick people in the world, and why those who are sickest and have the most serious trouble with teeth and skin and digestion, seem to be just those people who are doing the most drastic and unprecedented things to make themselves well: "The final end of your quest will be a kind of heaven-on-earth, a new sense of the wonderful powers of your mind and the splendid natural resourcefulness of your body to get and stay well. . . .

"So long as you continue in this high state of diet fitness, you will not be likely to have colds, coughs, flu, pneumonia, and the like, nor rheumatism, neuritis, nervousness, neurasthenia. You will be comparatively free from all fatigue, weariness, low vitality, and be practically assured of no heart failure, high blood pressure. In short you will have no likelihood of contracting any disease of any kind or description. There will be no necessity of surgery or loss of time in the hospital and you will be practically assured of longevity with mental and physical comfort. You will have a peculiar feeling of courage and aggressiveness in your work-life with increasing fondness for people and association with them daily, as well as a new sense of the spiritual values of all your life interests." It is not a coincidence that those who give up the guidance of their own good instincts and follow the advice of Dr. McKeever, and of the magazines of Hearst and Macfadden, need to be given a religion of food which promises a heaven in which there will be no "colds, coughs, flu, pneumonia, and the like, nor rheumatism, neuritis, nervousness, neurasthenia . . . fatigue, weariness, low vitality . . . heart failure, high blood pressure . . . likelihood of contracting any disease of any kind or description . . . necessity of surgery or loss of time in the hospital" and where "longevity with mental and physical comfort" "will be practically assured." This type of heaven is in point of fact better gotten through religion than through dieting, because, unfortunately, when one diets by these methods and those of Macfadden and *Modern Living*, and *Good Housekeeping*, one may irretrievably ruin one's health before the experiment is over and despaired of. On the other hand, looking for a heaven of universal amity and benevolence, with especial rewards vouchsafed to the clergy and to imperial and kingly personages, and the members of the secular and papal peerages, via revealed religion, at least leaves one the possibility of choosing a safe and healthful and natural diet while the expectations of a salvation are being cultivated via ritual, prayer, communion with the infinite, theosophy or Christian Science, or whatever method is adopted.

The principal trouble with the McKeever and other diets of these peculiarly and unnaturally limited and pseudonatural types is that they are rich in the vitamins one doesn't especially need, weak in those and in the minerals which are important, and positively menacing in the high level of acid, sugar, fat, cellulose or bulk intake which they call for. It is a favorite illusion of the food cultist that while cane or beet sugar or glucose is very bad for him, he can eat all he chooses of the same class of substances, if he will but absorb them through an orange or a banana or a bowl of honey and cream; whereas to receive one's fat or protein through a stewed chicken or rabbit or a rare roast of beef, would, according to these zealots, be flying in the face of nature. To those who have this curious view should come the reminder that a roast of beef or of fowl is precisely as *natural* a food and is a much richer storehouse of the elemental substances required, used and usable in the *human* body than any dish of bran and cream or honey or any orange or grapefruit or any head of cauliflower or Iceberg lettuce.

Raw foods have their place, but we are deprived of some of the most important sorts by what are conveniently termed "commercial necessities." Of other raw foods, such as oranges and grapefruit, pineapples and lettuce, we get far too much, also because of commercial necessities. One point which renders into something pretty close to nonsense the vitamin and natural diet pretensions of professional nutrition experts and food cultists, is their non-recommendation of raw milk, which most of the infants and children among us practically are not permitted to have, because it better suits the convenience of the great milk distributors and their friends, the health officials, and other medicos, to assert that pasteurization (cooking) is necessary to assure a germ-free milk supply. The real fact is that pasteurization as an almost universal requirement of milk distribution in cities removes the small milk distributor from the market and throws the business, and a very big business indeed, right into the lap of those who own or control pasteurization plants and can afford the expensive paraphernalia of milking machines, cream separators, chemical supplies, and bottling and capping machinery. It is the custom of the propagandists for large-scale milk distribution to urge that a return to small-scale operation and unpasteurized milk would be a decision to produce dirty, diseased, and insanitary milk, a line of reasoning which seems adequately negatived by the experience in other trades. It was not a *little* bakery that, in Westchester County, New York, in April 1935, caused the illness of 800 to 1200 consumers of cream puffs (for fuller discussion see Chapter IX); it was a mass-production bakery of the first magnitude, with all the advantages of "sanitary" large-scale production; it just happens that for business reasons those advantages *are not really available in bakeries and other great mass production food plants, and are not effective to protect the public health.* Their real function, in the bakery trade as in milk distribution, is to give big business advantages over little business, and business as a class, advantages of a very dangerous character over consumers as a class. The vogue for oranges, lemons, and grapefruit is another such technique. Ask your nutritionist and home-economics friends why, if raw fruit juices are so important, business does so little to make raw instead of heated milk available to the children of the people of low income. And why, if raw fruits and vegetables are so vitally necessary, nutrition and home-economics workers have not concerned themselves to provide a supply of apples and pears of which the part just under the skin, where the raw-fruit vitamin is concentrated, can safely be eaten, rather than discarded as is now necessary on account of the spray residue poisons. And why, if the raw-fruit and raw-vegetable vitamin is so necessary, nutrition workers do not put their personal efforts and the efforts of their professional societies to the problem of getting raw fruits and vegetables that are safe to eat, and free from the poisonous arsenical dust and spray residues that now coat cabbage, broccoli, and cauliflower to such degree that their consumption has brought deathly illness to hundreds and death to some. The writer advises that his readers postpone their interest in raw fruits and vegetables until such time as the experts get around to concerning themselves with these problems, and showing by their deeds rather than their papers on guinea pig experiments, their genuine concern for raw foods of a kind and quality that are fit to eat—for oranges, lemons, and grapefruit, for example, that are ripe and not artificially colored to imitate ripeness. That will be time enough for consumers to think seriously about the raw fruit problem, after the experts have given the subject thorough, rather than California-fruit-grower, and rat-and-guinea-pig, consideration.

IX

BREAD—MODERN CORRUPTION OF AN ANCIENT TRADE

There are a number of great industries which have contributed in very special measure to the debasement, not only of the American dietary, but what is even more important, to the corruption of dietary common sense and good judgment of every one of us. Highest amongst these trades must perhaps be placed the commercial bakeries and their chief suppliers of raw materials, the flour millers and the sugar refiners; next perhaps follow ice cream and soft drinks and candy. The special skill of the bakers has turned from a once respected and respectable trade to a degree of adulteration and sophistication which is now so widespread and so pervasive that all sensitiveness to the question of quality and healthfulness and dietary adequacy in bakery products has been lost; and with a few rare exceptions, which are always, this writer believes, among the small, old-fashioned baker's shops found occasionally in small towns and cities, a commercial bakery is about the last place one would visit to find out how to make good, honest, wholesome bread, rolls, cakes, or cookies free from dubious or palpably unwholesome additions of chemicals. This subject is treated at some length in *100,000,000 Guinea Pigs;* yet information subsequently received would indicate that the authors of that book considerably understated the case against the commercial baking industry. J. B. Matthews and R. E. Shallcross, in

Partners in Plunder, also had much to say of this benighted trade and its ever-worsening circle of abuses of consumers' rights and consumers' digestions. They cite for instance the case of the official discovery in North Dakota that little, if any, true whole wheat or graham bread was being sold, the appearance of whole wheat being achieved in some cases by artificial coloration.

Even the reactionary journal, *Food Industries*, normally most ready to gloss over any food industry's sins, is clear on the low repute in which public opinion holds the baking trade. In its issue of December, 1934, *Food Industries* says: "The baking industry probably will have to explain why its products taste so differently from those 'Mother used to make,' and justify the use of the many substitutes for the old fundamental ingredients home cooks have always used. This might enlighten the baker, as well as the consumer, as to why his bread is either a soggy mass of tasteless white stuff, or a dry and equally tasteless puff, composed mainly of the maximum number of air pockets." The problem of the consumer who eats bakery products is well summed up in a brief discussion in a Consumers' Research Handbook, here reproduced in part by special permission: Bakers in increasing number, and now almost the whole commercial baking trade "are using various substitutes for natural ingredients in the manufacture of their products, enabling them to keep large quantities of stock for long periods without spoilage, to improve appearance, and mainly to cheapen the food. For instance, egg or milk powders, skim milk and frozen eggs are frequently used. Pies and pastry fillings often contain far less of fruit than they do of starch 'fillers' or extenders. Artificial flavors and fruit acid substitutes are common to give taste or tartness. Artificial coloring . . . is added to

make breads and cakes appear to contain eggs; starch is
added as a filler; bluing [or even the laxative coal-tar drug,
phenolphthalein, very poisonous to some individuals] is used
to color icing; and in some cases cakes have actually been
shellacked [as candies commonly are], the shellac containing
arsenic." Especially hazardous to health "is bacterial decomposition resulting from the method of handling and keeping fillings for pies and cakes." Serious outbreaks of poisoning, involving sometimes a hundred persons or more, are of
not uncommon occurrence. "Moist mixtures of this kind
make excellent food for bacteria as well as tasty food for
humans. Bakery sanitation is generally at a very low level.
. . . Naturally, the vitamin and mineral contents of these
bakers' goods are practically nil, because the components of
the recipes are, almost without exception, processed, denatured and devitaminized substances used because of cheap-
ness, storage qualities, or commercial custom. . . . The national Food and Drugs Act is entirely inoperative in this
field, and the state and local acts are either quite out of date
with respect to the adulterations currently used, or are practically unenforced, as also in the fields of ice cream, soft
drinks and confectionery. . . ."

The industry's own journals tell enough of the story that
one would hardly need to read any further. For example,
in the *Baker's Helper* of September 24, 1932: "Because, for
many years, no one but the owner-baker ever entered a bakery and learned what was done—and not done,—because of
the time required, and because of the cost, bakery pans went
unwashed for so long that the tradition grew up that they
should not be."

One man wrote Consumers' Research thus: "Can you advise me regarding an acid, solution, or other bath that

should be used to remove the dirt from steel bread racks in a bakery? The accumulated dirt is largely flour dust, some sugar, etc., from cinnamon buns and other sweet goods— also no doubt a good deal of wax from the wax bread wrappers."

Another, a technical expert, approaching the problem from a quite different angle, says: "I have often been struck with wonder as to the quantity of tin and base metal introduced into baked goods thru the practice of bakers using mixers of the bowl type. During the mixing of a batch of cakes for instance, the bowl may be scraped down several times with a flexible spatula. The spatula being of steel wears to a less extent than the tin coating on the mixer bowl. Seldom does one see one of these mixer bowls from which all or most of the tin coating has not been scraped. In time of course the community eats the tin coating from these machines. Then the baker finds it necessary to grease the inside of the bowl every time he leaves the machine overnight to prevent rust formation. During the period ensuing [there is] wear on the base metal of the bowl and on the metal of the spatula. . . . The spatulas do wear, and they take on some pretty sharp edges. Occasionally they become so sharp that careless bakers may even cut themselves— another source of temporary contamination to the product."

The man who wrote this letter was not aware that the tin linings of food factory equipment are quite regularly contaminated with lead, often present in considerable quantities. The amount of lead which reaches the consumer's stomach via bakery goods must be enormous and gravely menacing to health, judging from the foregoing statement, which describes a typical condition; and from the fact recently disclosed by an analysis conducted for Consumers' Research,

that ammonium carbonate, used very commonly as a leavening (gas-forming) agent in certain baker's goods such as
cookies and cakes, contained, as obtained from a commercial
bakery in a large Mid-western city, the enormous and
threatening proportion of 70 parts per million of lead. The
early decline of vitality and the incidence of chronic disease
in people who live predominantly on products of the commercial bakery could be explained almost on this type of
finding alone. On the other hand, research in such contaminations is made very difficult so that a consumer's organization
has the utmost difficulty in even getting samples of the
very special and very peculiar materials used in the commercial baking industry—the various gelatinous pie-filling
mixtures, the highly colored and synthetic cornstarch cus-
tards that go into pies, éclairs and cream puffs, the special
low grades of chocolate, the dyestuffs, the egg powders, the
paraffin-like hydrogenated fats especially devised and distributed to commercial bakers and to them alone. Further
research into these problems must await the development of
satisfactory means of obtaining typical and representative
samples of the exact grades and kinds of these synthetic
and adulterated substances that bakers use, and the expenditure of the very considerable sums of money that would be
required to conduct the hundreds of thousands of delicate
chemical analyses that are needed. Unfortunately, since the
food and drug administrations of both federal and state
governments are almost uniformly blind on the side of their
heads which looks out toward the practices and ingredients
of the food-processing industries, the makers of bakery
goods, ice cream, soft drinks, soda fountain supplies, and
the like, it is almost hopeless to expect any help in this field
until Consumers' Research itself can get around to carrying

on more studies in the chemistry and toxicology of baker's supplies. Yet from the evidence of Congressional investigations, and of the commercial bakers' own trade and technical journals, a sufficiently alarming set of facts is easily to be gleaned.

Health officers, who do have full authority and could have the facilities and staff to examine and control raw materials used by commercial food factories, do not do so. Hardly one of them in the United States knows as much about questions of food contamination and poisoning as can be found in a fraction of the files of Consumers' Research; this is judged, as one has a right to judge, by health officials' characteristic failure to publish scientific and technical researches and findings of fact in the field, and by their singularly unscientific and unsocial conduct in many other ways, exhibited in the scandals that occur in the frequent cases of poisoned éclairs and lead-arsenate poisoned vegetables and fruits. Such cases, when too flagrant and involving too many deaths, do sometimes break through the wall of silence with which newspapers and magazines and radio surround the existence of grave hazards to consumers and the sporadic or slow poisonings to which consumers are subjected.

Two instances that can be briefly related tell the tale of the health officer's tender solicitude for his local business interests or for business in general, and his amazing dullness in that part of his mind which might be employed in the service of the public constituency that pays his often generous salary.

California has long had an exceptional amount of food poisoning from arsenic and lead remaining on fruits and vegetables as a spray residue. Altogether hundreds of cases of persons taken seriously ill have been reported, and the fear of poisoning from cabbage, broccoli, and other vegetables became so serious at times as to be a distinct menace to the commercial marketers of truck-garden products. In one case food poisoning had affected more than 100 persons in three widely separated parts of Los Angeles County and serious illnesses were daily breaking into headlines locally; news stories were even being sent out by the Associated Press. In this emergency, Dr. Charles Decker, city health officer, publicly "deplored the broadcast statements that arsenic insect spray on vegetables was responsible for the poisoning." He preferred to believe that something else must have caused the trouble, for example, a "tainted sauce used on the vegetables." Said Dr. Decker: "The shouting about arsenic spray poisoning caused a loss of hundreds of thousands of dollars to vegetable growers in Los Angeles county. Practically every vegetable we use is sprayed to keep insects or bacteria away. In delivering the product growers are required to remove the outer covering when necessary to make certain that none of the insecticide is present.

"It is very seldom that poison spray is used in such quantities as to cause injury. It is very regrettable that the entire vegetable industry in this area should be damaged by the uncurbed statements that spray causes poisoning unless it is very certain that such is the case. Proper inspection by the county is the main thing necessary."

But Dr. Crandall, health officer for the county in the Santa Monica Bay district, said he had no doubt that the "malady suffered by the seven guests at the beach club [three of whom were in an extremely critical condition] was the result of a poison spray." He "gave a lengthy statement which contained cautions on the proper washing of vegetables and he suggested that apparently truck gardeners were using a spray with a stronger arsenic content than allowed by Federal law." (But Federal law does not limit the arsenic content of the sprays, and a health officer should know that.)

Dr. Decker's statement, the one first quoted, contains a number of major errors, such that if he is correctly quoted, his unfitness to serve as a health officer in a region menaced by arsenic and lead poisoning of consumers of garden produce is clearly established. It turned out that, in spite of Dr. Decker's reported attempts to whitewash the vegetable growers, arsenical insecticide residues were indeed the cause of the illness of those who ate broccoli.

Poisoning by arsenic-sprayed lettuce was so prevalent that an Altadena resident, the owner of more than 300 monkeys, declared that half of his monkeys became ill and that altogether he had lost by death eight monkeys, two swans, and a dozen other birds by feeding them lettuce. The whole situation was so serious that "approximately 125 complaints [were] received by the county health offices by persons made ill by eating poisoned vegetables during [a period of] 60 days and 37 growers, mostly Japanese, [had] been arrested." Yet the health officer's official reaction was anger at the financial loss to the commercial vegetable growers of the county.

In the case of the 800 to 1200 people poisoned by cream puffs and chocolate éclairs sold from the Cushman's Sons, Inc., bakery in the fashionable Westchester, suburban county north of New York, not only was there no prosecution of the bakery officials, but the offending éclair factory came in for exactly the same sort of whitewashing as did the fruit and vegetable markets in Los Angeles. Said Dr. Nicoll, health commissioner of Westchester County: "The eggs were received from a national distributer [sic] in Chicago, and were laid in Missouri. They were packed in Nebraska. We could not prosecute the distributer [sic] here, but when we have the evidence we may turn it over to the Federal authorities.

"None of the other products of Cushman's Sons, Inc., was affected. We have inspected the bakery and the men who handled the food and found everything first rate. The company voluntarily has discontinued the cream product until Fall. This sort of thing could happen to any company, no matter how clean the plant. We need more food inspectors in Westchester." (From a report in the New York *Times*.)

One would hardly expect it to occur to a Westchester County health official that eggs received from a national distributor in Chicago, that had been laid in Missouri and packed in Nebraska could not possibly be successfully controlled by an additional health inspector or two in Westchester County, New York. Dr. Nicoll failed to explain why, in a matter of such vital moment, it was not in order to make public the name of the national distributor in Chicago and of the packer in Nebraska, along with the name of Cushman's Sons, Inc., the bakery through whose carelessness or lack of proper control of their raw materials the epidemic of poisoning occurred. It is also not clear why, if the plant was perfectly clean, as Dr. Nicoll's statement implies, more food inspectors would help to solve the problem (unless indeed he feared, as he well might, that some other bakery where everything was "first rate" too, would in due time poison its customers).

Indeed, so far beyond the possibility of better control by health inspectors was the great Cushman plant, according to Dr. Nicoll's own statement made at another time, that, ac-

cording to one news story, the "distributors of the suspected
pastries [were] given a clean bill of health and considerable
praise by Dr. Nicoll and his deputy commissioner, Dr. Edward L. Marsh,[1] following a tour of inspection of the company's plant at White Plains. . . .

" 'It was the cleanest bakery I have seen,' Dr. Marsh
said." Dr. Nicoll also said: "An examination of the premises
of the factory by this department showed a well-run estab-
lishment operated in a cleanly, sanitary way." What Dr.
Nicoll might have said had he been a little more frank was
that, so far as his knowledge of food control went, there
wasn't much you could do about infected canned egg yolks
from eggs laid in Missouri, sold by a national distributor
in Chicago, and marketed from Nebraska. Had Dr. Nicoll
had more respect for the intelligence of his audience, he
would not have suggested that this geographic combination
ending in Westchester County, New York, could have been
remedied by any so simple a solution as a few more inspectors in Westchester—or anywhere else, indeed.

As to the general low grade of baker's ingredients, the
English journal, *Food Manufacture*, in an article on "The
Manufacture of Fruit Jellies in the U. S. A.," says: "A surprisingly large amount of 'imitation jelly' is made in the
U. S. A. The ingredients employed are pectin, acid, sugar,
colour and flavoring material. [Not fruit, please note!]
Cherry, strawberry, and raspberry are the most popular
flavouring, the jelly being largely distributed in bulk to
bakers, and used in jelly rolls (similar to jam rolls in Eng-

---

[1] The correct name and initials of the deputy commissioner of Westchester County are Edward H. Marsh instead of Edward L., as the
newspaper had it.

land). The low cost of this type of jelly is the only point in its favour, as the synthetic flavour is usually very pronounced."

An official of the U. S. Treasury Department writes in an official letter: "Process or renovated butter is defined by law to mean butter which has been subjected to any process by which it is melted, clarified, or refined and made to resemble genuine butter. It is principally used by bakeries." Needless to say, such butter is not butter at all in any proper sense; it is in proper terms the chemical end-product of a debased trade which uses spoiled butter as one of its raw materials.

Lest anyone doubt the practical importance in the trade of this type of butter, one may cite an advertisement of the Blue Valley Creamery Co. in the *Bakers Weekly* that referred to bakers who were "reluctant to use the so-called 'baker's butter'—the reconstituted, near-rancid, distress products that clutter up the market."

In the *Congressional Record,* Congressman Patman quotes a Tariff Commission Report in reference to the 60,000,000 pounds of coconut and palm kernel oils consumed annually by the confectionery and baking trade, thus: "Confectioners and bakers state that if necessary they would be willing to pay a price premium for coconut and palm kernel oils for many types of fillings and coatings."

Thirty per cent of the coconut oil pressed from dried copra, produced in Dutch East Indies, the Philippines, Ceylon, under conditions of incredible human servitude and oppression, and under sanitary conditions which render absolutely absurd any pretensions to cleanliness of plant and methods on the part of any baker who uses it, is said to go into "vegetable butter, . . . used widely as a butter substitute in candy making, bakeries." (*Trend*, December 30, 1933.)

Canned or frozen egg yolks are used in commercial cakes. "A product known as 'Eggrowhite,' produced by a Baltimore firm, was seized and destroyed by the Department [of Agriculture] because the dried egg albumen which it gave the impression of containing exclusively was adulterated with an approximately equal quantity of starch, and also because it contained saponin, a foaming agent frequently associated with poisonous substances, which might have rendered it deleterious to health. The manufacturer produces bakers' and confectioners' specialties and it is presumed that the product was intended for consumption in these fields."

Brolite, advertised in *Bakers Weekly*, has " 'the follow-through flavor.' . . . [It helps] yeast goods retain that good butter aroma and taste. . . . It fixes and supports the rich, delicate flavor of butter in your products and keeps them tasting delicious up to the time of eating. Now—with the cost of butter rising—is the time to investigate BROLITE."

Badex is advertised to improve "crust color, giving it a rich brownness."

An advertisement for *Nusoy* says, "In standard white bread, 1½% *Nusoy* requires 4½% added moisture."

Lecithin is another raw material coming into common use in commercial bakeries. The claim is made for it that it "distinctly increases the elasticity of gluten flour and that it is possible to use 50 per cent more water in the dough."

Ceresalts "for treatment of baking waters" is advertised as insuring "the necessary degree of permanent hardness in water used for the manufacture of any food product." As to

what Ceresalts is and what it might do to the customer's
insides, how poisonous or non-poisonous it may be, and
how well, if at all, it may be controlled in manufacture and
use to prevent contamination with metallic poisons, the
user of course is in no position to know, any more than the
consumer of one of the widely-sold process cheeses can know
whether he would approve of the ingredients that are used
to make it, and the kind of cheese and milk by-products that
go into its manufacture.

Gum tragacanth, gum acacia, and citrus pectin are added
to commercial cake batter, because then the cake retains
moisture better and shows less tendency to get stale. "Uniform distribution was obtained by mixing powdered gum
in a non-aqueous medium [cottonseed or coconut oil, perhaps?] before adding it to water or milk to effect the hydra-
tion [incorporation of water]."

Dainty Super-Cake Flour is advertised as "capable of
carrying unusual amounts of sugar. . . ." "It is called
'Sugar-Safe' because it safely carries the higher ratios of
sugar and other enriching ingredients."

Procter & Gamble Company of Ivorydale, Ohio, "to protect 'Sweetex,' a new cake shortening . . . has taken out a
patent covering the production of cakes containing more
sugar than flour. . . . The invention covered by the patent
consists in adding small quantities of lecithin and free fat-
ting [sic; fatty is meant] acids to the shortening, whereby
it becomes possible greatly to increase the amount of sugar
used in a cake without undue tendency of the cake to 'fall.'
. . . At the same time the proportion of milk or other liquid
constituents in the cake may be increased, resulting in cakes
of unusually fine texture and eating and keeping qualities.
. . . Whereas the invention is said to be of little value as

applied to cakes made with whole eggs or egg yolks, it is understood to be *especially effective in cakes containing little or no egg yolks,* but principally egg whites. . . . Under these circumstances, *the proportion of sugar to flour may be increased above 100 per cent and even as high as 130 to 150 per cent.*" [Italics mine.]

An advertisement in *Bakers Weekly* for January 19, 1935, refers to *Vreamay* as "Swift's special new shortening"— "made specifically for use in the richer type of cakes carrying 120-180% of sugar."

The housewife who has read of the tremendous health values of prunes, and is willing to pay an extra price for prune bread, does not know of course that prunes which give a dark-colored bread help save in the baker's flour costs by permitting him to use flour of a less favored color than he could otherwise employ. From the consumer's standpoint, it is important to know that the cheaper, off-colored flour often comes from low-grade or contaminated or spoiled grain.

A physician discussing the problem of food allergy in relation to acne, remarks the uncertainty of the actual composition of rye bread, so called, and reports the work of an expert who determined that in Chicago there was no such thing as rye bread. It was found "that rye bread in Chicago contains anywhere from 10 to 60 per cent of wheat.

In North Dakota, little if any true whole wheat or graham bread was being sold by commercial bakers; yet "practically every baker makes a bread which," the report continues, "is labeled 'Whole Wheat Bread.' " The official food control officers report: "We have examined a number of these breads sold throughout the state during the past sev-

eral months and analysis shows that the amount of whole
wheat flour present varied all the way from 30% to 100%."

Food Industries reports "a bread improver that takes 200
per cent absorption." This miracle of changing water into
bread is performed under the property rights and restric-
tions of the Joe Lowe Corporation, Brooklyn, N. Y., the
patented legal adulterant being known as *Velvert*. The owner
states that "it produces fifteen more loaves per barrel of
flour." *Food Industries* comments that this product "im-
parts new characteristics to the loaf"; surely that goes
without saying. Each of a score of other common bakers'
adulterants makes its own peculiar contribution to "new
characteristics" of the bakers' loaves.

Commercial bread, never at a lower level of quality than
it is today, thanks to the ingenuities of such corporations as
that contriving *Velvert*, has drawn some scathing comments
from the food industry itself, an industry hardly to be
charged with bias in favor of consumers as against bakers.
"Somehow we cannot resist the devilish temptation," says
the editor of *Food Field Reporter*, "to advise bakers to put
strings on the prevailing 'balloon' loaves so the kiddies will
want to buy more of them, or put more bread and less air
in them so people will want to eat more of them." The few
Americans remaining who have any recollection of the taste
of good bread (and indeed there are few outside of rural and
small-town communities) will not need to be convinced that
commercialism with all of its chemical tricks in baking has
committed one of the major dietary crimes of this generation, and has contributed more to American ill-health than
anyone perhaps except the Bureaus of Entomology in the
federal and state governments, which have invented and dif-

fused the diabolical technique of spraying lead arsenate upon the major part of our fruit and vegetable supply.

The freedom of the baker to add foreign elements to his dough, usually with the purpose of increasing its water-absorbing capacity and consequently its weight or of increasing its porosity and consequently the size of the loaf, is practically unrestrained in this country. Many other countries, such as France and New Zealand, have put bakeries under control of the food and drug laws, and have placed strict prohibitions against these so-called "improvers" which are as a rule chemical artifices for giving the consumer less of a lower-grade food for more money. Though their purpose is to cheat the consumer, their effect may well be mildly to poison him with all of his intake of his principal foodstuff. *Like many another adulteration, their effect is selective against the poor.* Since bread is a cheap food, it forms a far larger part of the food supply of the poor than of the well-to-do, and makes perhaps the greatest contribution of all to the very poor health of the masses of underpaid and unemployed city and rural populations.

Among the latest inventions patented is the addition of gum karaya to baking powder which, according to *Food Field Reporter,* "results in increasing the viscosity of the dough in which the baking soda is used, thereby producing a greater degree of expansion than with ordinary baking powder, producing a more porous product, and permitting the manufacture of a given size of loaf with a smaller amount of flour and other ingredients." The patent for this latest trick of puffing up bread which requires less of the chemicals (apparently meaning the chemicals used as yeast foods) "so that a . . . loaf is produced of great lightness and porosity," was issued to Standard Brands, Inc., under the amazing title "Composition of Matter and Process of Producing Porous Material." The "object of this invention is to produce a more porous resultant product or one occupying a greater volume for a given weight. A further object of this invention is to permit the manufacture of a given size loaf with a smaller amount of flour and other iningredients." Standard Brands' research men, like thousands of their scientifically trained colleagues in other business concerns, have the choice of working against the interests of consumers or seeking employment elsewhere at lower pay and with less economic security.

The brazen *ne plus ultra* of the baking industry is the current laxative bread. "Two slices a day keeps constipation away—baked by secret formula formulated by Edward Owen, endorsed by mothers everywhere," runs the advertisement of the Becker Bread Company, of East St. Louis. Analysis disclosed that the secret formula contains the harmful drug phenolphthalein whose continued use (either in bread or in *Ex-Lax*) may lead to chronic constipation. The laxative claims for this and that bread, usually based upon the addition of something which has no place in a consumer's honest loaf, have become so prevalent that steps are being taken in some states to prohibit the use of all such claims of laxative effect in advertisements of bread. California has already placed a ban upon such advertising. No state of course has set up legal and technical machinery for controlling the kind and quality of the ingredients themselves of the commercial bakeries' product. Such regulation is as unlikely under present political alignments as is successful elimination from the rates of privately owned gas and electric companies of excess profits and the costs of chicane and fake protests of investors to congress. Business everywhere, under the partnership of plunder of business and the Business-State, always manages in a few months or years to get into a position where it controls the controllers. The bread industry now has reached the same big-business attitude and toughness of ways of the big utility companies. It has powerful lobbies, special advertising and publicity and science tentacles into the schools and colleges, the newspapers and popular magazines, and nothing short of a consumers' boycott of the product of mass production bakeries can bring this industry to terms and start it again in the direction of baking bread instead of high-priced chemical fluff unfit to be fed to chickens.

X

THE COMMERCIAL BAKERY — AMERICA'S CONTRIBUTION TO THE ART OF FOOD-SPOILING

The adulterations used in commercial bakeries are too numerous even to list here, but a few more can be covered very briefly. Striking evidence of the bakers' attitude toward their products is found in articles and advertising in the trade journals, written with cold candor that is carefully excluded from the bakery advertisements read by the public in newspapers and magazines. A writer in *Bakers Weekly* suggests that bread will stay fresh longer if gelatinized starch, powdered gelatine or agar are added, though the author admits "the bad keeping quality of bread is generally the consequence of not using the best materials or not treating them with the best skill."

A quotation from the Technical Food News department of the *Food Field Reporter* illustrates the easy ways that are regularly found for covering deviations from home processes in the making of factory bread. "The typical aromatic flavor of bread baked by the sour dough method" may be obtained by adding propionic acid to the dough, or the "methyl, ethyl, butyl and amyl esters of propionic or other similar low aliphatic acids may be used." Who is to say that any or all of these interesting substances is fit for the bakery workman to handle (many bakery chemicals are not) and

163

for your stomach to digest? The same department of this
journal mentions in another place the new-found use of
hydrogen peroxide, the well known antiseptic, to raise bread!
Every sort of chemical substance and mechanical device is
being worked upon in an effort to reduce the use of yeast—
the one substance that has been commonly used in baker's
bread that has notable nutritional (as distinguished from
fuel or Calorie) value. Yeast is far too costly and incon-
venient to handle to be regarded as suitable for use in a
mass-manufactured product designed for the masses. Baker's bread has now been degraded everywhere to such an
extent that no one expects quality. The buyer must now
expect his bread to contain quack medicines such as vitamin
D, and the laxative, phenolphthalein; or "California Prune
Concentrate, the New Laxative Sensation for Use in Bakery
Products"; or he may be offered that new public menace,
"iodized bread," recently introduced in Wisconsin. All these
are magical ingredients and attributes that can be *advertised* and serve, in print at least, to distinguish one bread
factory's tasteless, watery, and airy bread from another's.
When commercialization and corruption of a trade's skills
and ingredients go so far as to eliminate yeast—the only
reason for eating bread instead of crackers and zwieback—
it is time to quit using the product of that trade. The commercial bakeries really do underestimate the intelligence of
their public, though as their trade press reveals, they clearly
think that impossible. The common man may not *know* why
he no longer eats as much bread as he did and as the baking
trade thinks he should, but he does dumbly and unknowingly
and painfully arrive at a solution that works for him, which
is to eat more of something else (quite likely also bad but not
so bad as factory bread). The bread-factory owners, forced

by declining profits, try to save their incomes by cheapening the bread still more, with yeast-savers, and butter-savers, and flour-savers and whiteners, and water-absorption-increasers, and anti-staling chemicals, and everything indeed but air-and-water-savers, till finally they are in the terrible stage where it is necessary to hire nutrition professors and movie stars to hold what ground remains. The final loss of confidence that will accrue to a debased product using debased methods of exploitation and debased science to keep it in consumption against the common man's better sense and native instinct for good food, will not be long in running what is left of the market. Nevertheless the New Deal administration's tenderness for the big food processors will still keep bread on the must list of those on relief and those others who must feed on the bounty of government, even if the vile stuff is disdained, and must be thrown away as refuse.

The good, healthy, farm-kitchen smell of the old-fashioned housewife's home-baked bread must be worrying business men a good deal; perhaps it represents the last barrier of consumer good sense and childhood memory which must be defeated (with the aid of the women's magazines, home-economics "research," and the schools) to bring about that happy time when everyone will be content to eat flavorless and insipid and vitaminless bread. When the last citizen who remembers the scene and odor in grandmother's kitchen is gone, or hors de combat on account of being poisoned into senile decay with adulterations and substitutions, the problem of consumers' sales resistance will disappear, even though the bakery's customers pass to their reward.

Experts of the Lucidol Corporation are reporting on the "effects of adding acetylmethylcarbinol to bread doughs to improve flavor of resulting bread. They regard this compound as responsible for much of the favorable flavor in most yeast-raised breads and have applied for patents covering use of the substance under conditions that provide uniformly good flavor in the finished loaf."

Our children and our children's children may never know the flavor of honest bread made of healthful materials, but at least Big Business and Big $cience will let them live and love on propionic acid, amyl esters, and acetylmethylcarbinol, and on that special lift of body and soul that comes from *Camel* and *Old Gold* cigarettes. This author is prepared to set it down as a safe prophecy that if the degradation of essential foodstuffs goes on much longer, if the staff of life becomes a straw or a husk, the next generation is going to have a very special *need* for cigarettes. Whereas now *Old Gold* and others find occasion to speed up the smoking habit among children in their 'teens, the exploiters of brandy, whiskey, and absinthe will find a ready market among the children in high schools and in summer camps who, when they need pure, unsophisticated food, get, quite unknown to themselves and their parents, "*Keystona*, the brown bread improver," *Arkady*, Ward's "yeast food" (*not* human food), gum tragacanth, gum karaya, *Brolite*, and coconut oil. The most sardonic, nay insane, aspect of this whole issue is that while farmers starve for lack of a market, consumers starve for lack of the very things the farmers are unable to sell *on account* of *Arkady, Keystona, Nusoy, Nulomoline*, and the rest of these products which are the characteristic and invariable means by which, under mass production, the factory owner (*not* the factory worker) takes both from the producer and the consumer. From the producer, the factory owner takes by withdrawal in whole or in part from his customary market; and from the consumer by delivering air and water and chemicals where *food* had been expected and was paid for.

A very brief digest of the atrocities that take place in commercial bakeries against the consumer who must eat the product, if based only on material in Consumers' Research's files, would take many more pages than can be given in this book. In the space available, it is possible only to list, in addition to those already mentioned, a few of the major adulterations and deviations from good home-kitchen practice, in respect to the making of commercial bakery bread, cakes, pies and other products.

Talk About Getting More Volume—That Is, You, the Customer, Pay More Money and Get Less Food

In the quotations which follow the emphasis related to the headings, indicated by italics, is mine unless otherwise noted.—F. J. S.

". . . *Bakerite* improves your best. It creams easier, *holds greater volume. . . .*" (From an advt. of *Bakerite* in *Bakers Weekly*, Feb. 9, 1935.)

". . . Cerelose [glucose] . . . gives it [a coffee cake] a definitely *larger volume. . . .*" (From advt. of Corn Products Refining Co. in *Bakers Weekly*, Jan. 20, 1934.)

"Let us show you how you can make pound cake with plenty of *volume*, beautiful grain and texture and wonderful *keeping qualities*. Because Brown's Hungarian Cake Flour carries *more moisture and sugar*." (From an advt., "Don't Let Pound Cake Worry You," of *Brown's Hungarian Cake Flour* in *Bakers Weekly*, Feb. 10, 1934.)

"*Dainty Super-Cake Flour* . . . a 'sugar-safe' cake flour [that] safely [can] carry more than 140%

sugar. . . . Cakes . . . of . . . fluffy down-like texture and *excellent* volume." (From an advt. for *Dainty Super-Cake Flour* in *Bakers Weekly*, Mar. 16, 1935.)

"Because Covo takes up more water, you get icings of greater volume that stay fresh far longer." (From an advt. of Lever Brothers Company in *Bakers Weekly*, Jan. 20, 1934.)

"A little added to any of your regular icings will make it lighter, more pliable and *it will cover more surface. Packaged cakes will not sweat or stick to wrapper.*" (From an advt. of *Frosty Fondant*, in *Bakers Weekly*, Feb. 9, 1935.)

Talk About Maintaining Freshness or Improving Durability of Bakers' Goods

Note the want of concern for purity of ingredients, home quality materials and processes. The baking trade employs the ingenious and deceptive sales tactics of the rug merchant or vacuum cleaner salesman. Home-baked products, to seem fresh, must *be* fresh; in baker's goods "freshness" is a product of the skills of chemists and engineers. The object: to provide a product built to stand wear and tear, weather, and time.

"*Bakers* have discovered that Science *has* produced a *better* shortening! (All-Hydrogenated) After years of research and years of test—we have perfected an all-hydrogenated, pure vegetable shortening that measures up to the most exacting requirements of the baking industry —a shortening now quite universally accepted as possessing *six definitely proved superiorities:*

1—Absolute uniformity—insured by constant laboratory control.

2—Superior keeping qualities; baked goods remain fresh longer.

3—Better creaming qualities—and holds its greater volume.

4—Plastic and workable, producing a finer texture. . . ."
(From an advt. for *Bakerite* in *Siebel Technical Review*, Oct. 1932.)

In advertising to the trade, the manufacturer does not trouble to emphasize the bunk about extra digestibility of the vegetable shortening that fills such a necessary—and misleading—place in advertising copy about shortening written for the ultimate consumer reader.

"Nulomoline—The Honey of Sugar. It keeps cakes from premature drying and hardening. The *continued freshness* emphasizes the quality the housewife appreciates." (From an advt. for *Nulomoline* in *Siebel Technical Review*, Jan. 1933.)

". . . Covo's *amazing keeping qualities*. . . . The other shortenings fell down—one by one they turned rancid. Covo was still fresh and sweet *after weeks of steady, merciless heat!*" (From an advt. for *Covo* of Lever Brothers Company in *Bakers Weekly*, Jan. 20, 1934.)

What research means in the baker's trade:

"For example, cake keeps such a short time that it actually is a worth-while improvement when someone discovers how to add one day to its freshness period." (From an article in *Confectioners Journal*, Feb. 1934.)

"He [Wm. Hefler of Boston, president of the New England Bakers' Association] refuses to load the stores on

Monday for Saturday's selling—*a remarkable feat for a wholesale cake merchant.* . . ." (From an article "Potomac States Bakers in Excellent Convention" in *Bakers Weekly*, Feb. 10, 1934.)

"We do not believe in small lots of any product. Rather than try to make all our variety in one day, and only have a dozen or two of each item, we carry our varieties over a period of a week and make them in quantity. In my experience the hardest item to sell is something you've only got a few of. If you have a hundred dozen, the last three or four dozen are hard to move because the display appeal has been lost." (From an article "Competing Successfully with the Housewife," by the head of the DeLaurent Bake Shops, Inc., Bridgeport, Conn., in *Bakers Weekly*, Feb. 10, 1934.)

It would be hard to find two more apt examples of the type of thing which has brought our food supply down to its present low quality. The business heads of the bakery business, and the bakery engineers alike, of which there is a considerable group with a professional society of its own, focus their thinking always upon modes of facilitating and cheapening mass production. They have not for many years considered what, in a differently ordered society, would be the prime job of the baker: to make *good* bread that is palatable and, above all, wholesome and nutritious. The mass production and distribution basis of commercial baking requires a long time between baking of its products and their consumption in the home. A wholesale baker's cake sold via the grocery store will be four days old before it reaches the customer and five and a half days old before it is eaten.

The baker's view of bread as a simple product with what

are primarily cash-register values is well illustrated by the following likening of bread to cement:

"BREAD is like CEMENT in THIS way! Some cements dry in a day. Others stay plastic indefinitely. . . .

So with breads. Their keeping qualities depend on the ingredients which make up the dough. For instance, the 'standard ingredient' used to keep loaves fresh longer is Badex. Bakers who use it avoid stale returns because Badex mellows the harsh gluten. . . . The result is a . . . uniform lace-like texture that retains its fresh feel." From an advt. of *Badex* in *Bakers Weekly*, Feb. 9, 1935.)

"Even if these products [sugar wafers and sandwich crackers] do not reach the ultimate consumer until many weeks after they have been baked, the coconut oil cream fillings do not become rancid, brittle, or unpalatable from the development of objectionable tastes characteristic of most of our domestic fats or oils when subjected to temperature conditions similar to those under which these products must be handled." (From an article "The Case of Coconut Oil—Politics or Science?" by J. D. Craig, Spencer Kellogg & Sons, in *Soap*, Jan. 1933.)

"While I do not know the formula and cannot get it until I decide whether or not to put any money in same, but I can say this much. He tells me it [a formula for producing frosting commercially] has 3 pounds of sugar and 1 pound of glucose (that ratio), and the different flavors are maple, strawberry, chocolate, vanilla and others. . . . He claims it is pure and that he has been in this business for twenty-seven years, *that it will keep indefinitely and not mold.*" (From a letter to one of the authors of *100,000,000 Guinea Pigs.*)

Talk About Getting and Holding More Water in the Dough
    (Water at Bread and Cake Prices Is the Principal
    Technique That Has Been Used to Make Rich Bakers
    Richer and Poor Ones Poorer, and Has Made Poor
    Bakers of Them All)

"Perhaps, of greatest value is the hygroscopic property
of invert sugar. It attracts moisture to itself and to the
products in which it is used. Exposed under normal conditions that exist in New York, it always remains wet, and
if dried will attract about 15% of its weight of water.
For these reasons, it inhibits drying in baked goods and
prolongs their freshness. It prevents checking in cookies
and cuts losses caused by breaking." (From an article
"Invert Sugar in Baking," by John Godston of The Nulomoline Co., New York City, in *Siebel Technical Review*,
Jan. 1933.)

"A recent use for lecithin is its application to commercial baking. It is claimed that lecithin distinctly increases
the elasticity of gluten flour and that it is possible to use
50 per cent more water in the dough. . . . It produces an
even crumb, larger volume, and a distinctly longer life in
baked goods." (From an article "Lecithin in Baking" in
Food Manufacture, Aug. 1933.)

". . . the bakers' old trouble of cakes drying out too
quickly can now be overcome by adding a suitable quantity
of lecithin." (From an article in *Food Manufacture*, Aug.
1933.)

"Pure Idaho potato flour Holds Fast to Moisture . . . possesses the ability to take on moisture
rapidly. . . . The added moisture carried into your
loaf by Pure Idaho Potato Flour. . . ." (From an

advt. for *Lactivator* ["correctly proportioned butter-milk and potato flour"] in *Bakers Weekly*, Jan. 20, 1934.)

"Paniplus-made bread has added freshness because the *extra water necessary* in Paniplus doughs is structural water and does not bake out or dry out." (From an advt. of *Paniplus*—"not a yeast food" in *Bakers Weekly*, Feb. 9, 1935.)

"The formula for Virginia Treat Cake is about 40% liquid ingredients . . . because of the ability of *mfb*-51 [a Wesson Oil product] to take up this extra liquid in the form of eggs and milk (or water). . . . This accounts for the fact that Quik-Blend cakes will stay fresh fully 4 or 5 days.

"Virginia Treat Cake, like all Quik-Blend formulas, can be mixed in ½ the usual mixing time. This particular mix was put into the oven in 8½ minutes. . . . The cost of the mixing time is cut in half . . . will not cripple during the icing process because it is not as brittle as the ordinary type of layer. . . ." (From an advt. for "Formula *mfb*-51," in *Bakers Weekly*, Mar. 2, 1935.)

A Look at Some of the Curious and Low Grade Ingredients Used by Commercial Bakers (Who Include Many that Talk of "Home-Made Baked Goods")

Excerpt from a letter from a professor in a leading agricultural college:

"In bakery goods, there is found a considerable array of artificial things, especially dried egg white, artificial flavors and artificial colors, all these being established usages of the trade. Of all the utter follies in foods, it has

always seemed to me that the worst offenders were the
bakers, because they have seemed to set out to make their
products taste as poor as possible, whereas it would be a
simple matter for them to put a stop to practically all
home baking if they would make their products better.
There are many good reasons for buying bakery goods
instead of baking at home, because of high costs of gas
[at retail, to *ultimate consumers*] and the like and the
bother of making small amounts for the average home, but
one tires so soon of bakery products that the bakers are
not doing what they might easily and honestly do. Of
course there has been a great increase in the buying of
bakery products of recent years, but it might have been
far greater if the bakers had set out to make good things
to eat."

"Bill Johnson told us about a prominent society woman
in his town who chose his bread because she liked its extra
whiteness, zip and color brilliance. . . .

"NOVADEL—a process for the improvement and stand-
ardization of color [of the flour], scientifically controlled at the mill." (From an advt. "How Would *Your*
Bread Look on This Table" for *Novadel-Agene* in *Bakers Weekly*, Jan. 19, 1935.)

"A baker's pastry cream sours in one day; 'even benzoate of soda will not prevent this happening.'" (From an
item under heading "Your Question Box," in *Bakers
Weekly*, Sept. 17, 1932.)

"Question: L. B.:—Under separate cover I am sending
you a small pie. Could you please tell me what kind of pie
thickener is used? *I don't think it is cornstarch because*

cornstarch gets watery after one day and this pie filling stands up like gelatine, . . .

"Answer:—Perhaps you make up your filling in large quantity and then put it away until needed. If this is the case you must be sure to have the containers sterile. It is a good plan to sterilize them with live steam *or some other sterilizing substance* just before the filling is put into them. . . . It sometimes happens that fillings of this type liquefy through bacterial activity and by thorough sterilization this can be avoided." (From "Your Question Box," sub-head "Thickener for Strawberry Pie," in *Bakers Weekly*, July 9, 1932.)

In answer to a query:

"Possibly you have in mind the pie fillings being made with gelatine *which are so popular at this time*. If such is the case we would refer you to *Bakers Weekly* for Jan. 6, page 49, on which you will find a formula for a filling of this kind. . . ." (From an item headed "Chocolate Chiffon Pie" under the column "Your Question Box" in *Bakers Weekly*, Feb. 10, 1934.)

"The Kut Nut Company new colored chopped nut meats are offered as scientifically treated and colored to conform with the United States Pure Food and Drug Act. They aid in decorating, flavoring, and beautifying pastries, being usable both on the inside and outside of cakes and cookies. The colors of these chopped nut meats are orange, red, green, and chocolate." (From "Colored Nut Meats for Toppings or Cake Mixes" in *Bakers' Helper*, Sept. 8, 1934.)

As to the use of *Top-Ezy*, note the following from a recent advertisement:

> "*Economical to use . . . light in weight* and *covers more* than sliced or ground nuts . . . keeps bright, glossy and crispy *in all weather*." (From an advt. for *Top-Ezy* in *Bakers Weekly*, March 23, 1935.)

> "*Coconut oil*, pressed from copra (dried coconut meat), is next in importance to linseed oil, forms a large staple in the Spencer Kellogg line. 70% of it goes into lather & soapsuds. Remaining 30%, subjected to Schwarcman refining and rancidity removing rigors, becomes vegetable butter, is used widely as a butter substitute in candy making, bakeries. With almost similar properties and uses, palm kernel oil differs only in having a smaller content of volatile acids." (From *Trend*, Dec. 30, 1933.)

The article fails to note that coconut oil in soap, above a certain proportion of the total oil or fat content, causes skin irritation; no one has taken the pains to consider what coconut oil and products made from it, when they are introduced into the food supply, may do to one's insides. There are many other "food" products just as dubious.

> "Bakers, confectioners and other food manufacturers who now use butter might well experiment with plastic cream. . . . One has reason to expect . . . that plastic cream could be used in increasing quantities by the food industries as time goes on." (From an article, "Plastic Cream—A New Product Is on the Market," in *Food Industries*, April, 1934.)

In the baking trade butter is something other and something very much cheaper than it is in your kitchen.

"The problem placed before the Blue Valley research staff was to develop a butter equal to the finest table butter in quality standards, yet with a special character suited to cake baking. . . ." (From an advt. of *Blue Valley Cake Butter* entitled "16 Butters—yet only ONE is the perfect butter for cake" in *Bakers Weekly*, Feb. 10, 1934.)

Just how specialized is the problem of finding cheap butter for bakeries is seen by the following carefully worded description of the kind of butter that bakers use and housewives, if they can help it, never do:

" 'Packing stock butter' . . . is the term generally applied to butter originating on the farm in small lots, concentrated into larger lots by country stores, and subsequently shipped either to metropolitan dealers for ultimate sale for manufacture of bakery products, confectionery and the like. . . ." (Excerpt from letter of an official of the Federal Food and Drug Administration, Mar. 7, 1934.)

From an agricultural news letter for business men:

"Already the hunt is on in the leather, steel, pharmaceutical, airplane, glue, *confection*, *baking*, and other industries for substitutes for the taxable *agricultural* by-products now used in manufacturing."

Typifying the confectioners' and bakers' objections to the requirement of stating on the label the ingredients in their products, under the terms of proposed new food and drug regulation:

"In addition, the type of shortening employed may vary from vegetable to animal, according to price con-

sideration and the particular season of the year. . . ."
(From an article by Dr. Stroud Jordan in *Confectioners
Journal*, March 1934.)

"The next move was to compare a few recipes. The
leavening ingredient was the one that set me thinking. I
noticed that the formulas from the Elastex people specified Elastex shortening, but any kind of baking powder;
those from the Sunrise company called for Sunrise baking
powder and any kind of shortening. Maybe the reason
grandmother's cakes were generally successful was because
she used a leavening agent of known action, instead of any
baking powder, a surprise package of uncertain strength
and action time. . . . In our angel cake, the mixing problem sifted down to the chief constituent, egg white. The
easy mistake is to whip the albumen dry, thereby making
the cakes tough. . . . We fixed it up as Bunny's Cake
Store, specializing on home-made angel cake. *We didn't
swear it was home-made on the premises.* The flour barrels
and kitchen ware were left in plain sight *as scenery.* . . .
We didn't even pretend to bake on the premises *by that
time, because cake No. 1 had taken hold,* and nobody
asked what factory it came from or whether it contained
chemicals. . . . I had to check and double check on several batches before I got to the bottom of that mystery.
. . . I missed it because I did my *laboratory experiment-
ing* with shell eggs, broken one at a time. In the plant we
used canned egg white. Canned albumen separates into
watery and gelatinous parts, with the latter sticking to
the can. Hans said that the gummy white whipped up to
normal volume. I told him to use all gelatinous albumen in
one batch, and the cakes came out tough. That meant a

new item in the instructions. Canned egg white had to be
stirred like paint for uniform results.

". . . [We] weren't too happy about production costs.
It was a *straight piece of chemical research*. I had the
laboratory try a number of *stunts to increase the volume*
whipped from our expensive [canned] egg whites. . . .
When we varied the hydrogen-ion concentration a trifle,
up or down, before whipping, we got *a substantial increase
in volume, and hence more cakes per egg, with an appropriate saving*. . . . 'It's the icing,' they said. 'It tastes
fatty, and not very wholesome fat at that.' . . . It was
the shortening people who got us out of that jam. . . .
The icing had been absorbing odors from the doughnut
frier. Inclosing the doughnut department and ventilating
it were the only sure remedies. We should have tumbled to
it ourselves but I guess our olfactory nerves were fatigued
with frying smells. . . ." (From an article, " 'Boughten'
Cakes," by Willard Cook of Toronto, Canada, who "made
the ladies eat 'bought' cake and like it. . . . And cut a
little bonus cake for himself besides" in *Food Industries*
for May 1934. Italics mine.—F. J. S.)

". . . an information against the Emulsol Corporation,
Chicago, Ill., alleging shipment by said company in viola-
tion of the Food and Drugs Act, on or about September
3, 1931, from the State of Illinois into the State of Ohio,
and reshipment from the State of Ohio into the State of
New York, of a quantity of frozen eggs that were adul-
terated. The article was labeled in part: (Tag on can)
'Emulsol M. * * * A Superior Emulsifying Agent For
Baking * * * The Emulsol Corporation * * * Chicago.'
"It was alleged in the information that the article was

adulterated in that it consisted in part of a decomposed, putrid, and filthy animal substance. . . . The court imposed a fine of $25." (*Notices of Judgment Under the, Food and Drugs Act*, U. S. Dept. of Agriculture, Sept., 1934: Adulteration of frozen eggs. U. S. [v.] Emulsol Corporation. Plea of guilty. Fine, $25.)

"In this lumpy, discolored condition, cocoa is rather difficult to mix, but its quality has not actually been damaged, as it readily regains its natural state when blended homogeneously with other ingredients, when mixed into a bakery dough and baked, or when made into a syrup." (From an article, "There is Cocoa for Every Use," by Benjamin J. Zenlea in *Food Industries*, Sept. 1934.)

". . . Bakers *are* winning them back—by making bread the old-fashioned way . . . with milk . . . pure, whole, *full-cream* milk. . . . Bakery-Tested PARLAC *Powdered* Whole Milk." (From an advt. for *Parlac* of Borden Sales Co., Inc., New York City, in *Bakers Weekly*, Jan. 12, 1935.)

" . . . Flakolene . . . entirely eliminates the sticking of loaves to the pan, gives more bakings per application and helps to *add a beautiful color* to the crust of the loaf." (From an advt. for *Flakolene* in *Bakers Weekly*, Jan. 26, 1935.)

"Tainting of cakes and other perishable food products is frequently due to noxious exhaust gases [which when ethyl gasoline is used include the deadly poisonous metal, lead] emitted by delivery trucks." (From *Siebel Technical Review*, Jan. 1934.)

Does *real lemon juice* spell *powdered* lemon juice to you? Can lemon juice be powdered?

"Build up a big volume in lemon pies by using the safest, most convenient form of lemon juice . . . Merrell-Soule *Powdered* Lemon Juice. *No trouble.* No risk. And it makes the most delicious lemon pies.

". . . Hammer home to your customers the fact [?] that your lemon pies are made with *real* lemon juice." (From an advt., "want to know—What are your lemon pies made of?" of Merrell-Soule Powdered Lemon Juice, Borden Sales Co., Inc., New York City, in *Bakers Weekly*, Jan. 20, 1934.)

"In these days of production and mass distribution of foodstuffs, nobody believes that eggs are generally used in mass-produced cakes for example, along comes the very handy tartrazine and you can, if required, give an *appearance* of even the number of eggs specified in Mrs. Beaton's famous book." (From an article by a British aniline dye expert in an American trade journal: "Dyestuff Economics—Making, Naming, Pricing, Selling" in *Chemical Markets*, Aug. 1932.)

Through the whole fabric of modern big-scale food manufacture and distribution run two basic ideas; these appear everywhere as the trail of the serpent. If the farmers on the one hand and the consumers on the other ever in sufficient number catch on to these tricks, the end of our modern government-bolstered business regency is close at hand. Mr. Wallace, Secretary of Agriculture, knows these points well and for a time started to talk of them in his resounding Christian-philosophic speeches, when suddenly it was borne in upon him that it was only in appearance that the farming population were masters of the Department of Agriculture's policies. When all the outward appearances of the govern-

ment controls were weighed and a certain amount of looking
behind the scenes was done, it was brought home to Mr. Wallace that Big Business and Big Finance called the tune and
determined the publicity and the speeches of the officials of
his sometimes-for-farmers but mostly-for-business Department of Agriculture. Mr. Wallace ceased to speak critically
and boldly of the extortionate profits of the great milk
distributing companies and the other food processors and
marketers, and of the great loss of livelihood and economic
power suffered by farmers and consumers through these fat
returns relinquished to that group of middlemen whose real
and physical contribution to the preparation and distribution of food is least. (Or would be least, unless we must
count as real that nullity of function represented by the
advertising copy.) The time when Secretary Wallace stopped
being frank about distributors' profits was a time when his
boss in the White House was having a critical time trying
to get big business to support TVA and the Agricultural
Adjustment Program, and General Johnson's NRA, then
making the morbid and convulsive movements that preceded
dissolution. But Mr. Wallace would have been coerced to the
same answer and to follow the same policy at any other time,
and for exactly the same reason. His aide Dr. Tugwell too
had found that Big Business's oft-protested love for the
people did not imply belief in a consumer-protective revision
of a 30-year-old food and drugs act, now for two decades
shot so full of legal and judicial holes that its functioning
was reduced to a form and a fraud. (For details, see
100,000,000 Guinea Pigs.)

The recurring threads of big business technique against
farmers, and against consumers, are nicely illustrated by
the incident of Mr. Langford, manager of the Sanico Bakery
in Washington, D. C., who appeared to testify in a Senate

hearing on bread prices in 1931. Mr. Langford testified that in his opinion "75 per cent of the larger bakeries use Arkady." According to Senator Capper, "the patents covering these articles [such as Arkady] set forth that the purpose is to reduce the cost of baking by saving sugar and yeast and enabling the flour to absorb more water." When Senator Capper inquired of Mr. Langford whether he knew that Arkady, used in the Sanico Bakery, was intended to reduce the cost of baking by thus foisting upon the consumer more weight in water, the manager of the bakery concern replied, "I do not know that." A baker who confesses that he does not know the purposes of an ingredient universally used to cheapen production in his industry, well represents the state of intelligence or ethics (whichever you will choose to consider determined by his disclaimer) of America's chief bread-spoiling, farmer-despoiling trade. Producer and consumer alike get gypped by the chemical inventions of the modern bakery, which by providing *chemical* food for the yeast organism cheat the farmer of a part of his legitimate market for wheat.

Arkady, the invention of the far-seeing scientists of the Ward Baking Co., is indeed a food for the yeast, but it is made of chemicals that are decidedly not good for the consumer of large quantities of bread. *Arkady* and products of similar effect are used, due to the workings of competition and advertising in a technically ignorant and ethically insensitive trade, in practically all commercial breadstuffs. Not only does *Arkady* aid the baker to withhold 15% of the flour that would otherwise have been incorporated into his loaf, and to use less yeast and less labor in his plant, but it literally chemicalizes a food which of all foods most needs to be rich in the vitamins that go with free use of yeast, and be free from contamination. It is curious that the representa-

tives of the people in the Senate and in the government
departments see no cause for complaint or legislative remedy
in the cheating of *farmer and consumer*, by an invention that
cuts 15% off the wheat content of bread, and substitutes
water, air, and certain unwholesome chemicals for wheat and
yeast.

Farmers had better get in touch with the Secretary of
Agriculture and with the President too, on the selfish side of
their interest in agriculture. Consumers who tried to get in
touch with them on the ethical and economic side of this
problem of food adulteration as it affected consumers found
both of these officials invariably occupied with larger and,
to them, more interesting matters—what to government officials are known as affairs of state, but to officials of General
Foods and General Mills are more realistically known as
keeping the government in its place, and out of business.

The whole matter of cheating the farmer at the one end
and the consumer at the other end of the production-con-
sumption chain, is one on which Consumers' Research has a
great deal of information; in due time this will be compiled
into a book, the book Mr. Wallace might have written had
he been truly Secretary of Agriculture, instead of Secretary
for the Trades Selling the Products of Agriculture. Mr.
Wallace's work has represented unfortunately more the approach of a man who sees himself as a sort of middle-man
between Mr. Roosevelt and God and between Mr. Roosevelt
and the processing industries, than as one who functions as
Secretary of Agriculture. But then such an attitude can not
be complained of in a country where even bakers of the
world's worst and most dividend-producing bread open their
annual conventions with prayer, and the invocation by a
cleric of the divine blessing upon their operations.

XI

ANOTHER LOOK AT THE SCIENTISTS
—LEARNING, TOO LATE, WHAT
WE ALREADY KNEW

An example of the unreliability of much that passes for science in nutrition, and likewise of the gross errors that can be made by naive use of the indications of animal experiments is given by an authoritative study completed recently at Rockefeller Institute for Medical Research. For some years it had been held that lack of vitamin C, in addition to producing scurvy (in guinea pigs) also caused (in guinea pigs) a disease resembling the rheumatic fever of human beings. Now comes a report of careful tests at Rockefeller Institute to the effect that on human subjects, vitamin C neither prevented nor cured rheumatic fever and indeed had no relation to its cause. Other vitamin substances were tried also without benefit.

The author of this book has an idea based on fairly wide reading and observation in its field that many other supposed discoveries about vitamin C (all or nearly all based on guinea pig experiments) may turn out to be equally moonshine, along with its supposed effect on rheumatic fever. The too simple reasoning and experimentation of food scientists on vitamin studies is thrown into a funny light by a series of posters published by the U. S. Bureau of Home Economics, which does a great deal of work on vitamins, but not enough to enable it to see a joke in its own findings.

Chart 1 of the series of eleven posters begins with the

dangerous and largely untrue generalization "Growth is an Index of Nutrition," which will be discussed a little later in this chapter, and then continues, "White rats and other small animals are used for nutrition studies. Rats grow rapidly and mature early. *They eat the same kind of food we do and show the same effects of good and bad diet.*" [Italics mine.]

On succeeding charts, vitamins A, B, D, and G are demonstrated by pictures of rats deprived of the respective vitamin and of others which had plenty, but the effect of *vitamin C* ("For Healthy Gums and Teeth") is shown, without explanation of the shift of test animals, by a comparison of guinea pigs fed adequate amounts of vitamin C, and deprived of vitamin C. It would seem then that rats eat the same kind of food as human beings *except* when the importance of vitamin C is to be demonstrated. Then the rats seem to fall down and that strange beast, the guinea pig, not native to this climate or to our food supply, has to be brought in to help make citrus fruits and raw fruits and vegetables seem necessary to the food supply of human beings (as in fact they are not).

Scurvy-like symptoms are found in people who eat quantities of raw food, and many who never touch a raw fruit or vegetable have no touch or trace of it, but two such contradictory observations do not swim into the ken of persons who conduct nutrition experiments and who find pleasure and profit in helping the citrus fruit growers turn oranges and grapefruit into a daily necessity among the poor who have not money to buy them.

A parallel case on a smaller scale is that of an investigation of suspected canned meat given to people on relief, whose children suffered from digestive troubles. Local authorities had tested the meat on the evidence of mice and found it bad. The Federal Government, sensitive to the problem of fending off accusations that the New Deal administration was feeding bad meat to the poor, fed samples of the suspected meat to *cats* and found it good.

"Mice," say the Federal authorities, according to a publicity story from the Food and Drug Administration, "are not as dependable as cats for testing meat." If one animal does not give the answer that is needed, or one which an investigator thinks he needs, another animal can often be found that will make matters come out as they should, to favor the meat canners, or the orange or Iceberg lettuce growers, as the case may be.

Beware of nutrition workers, and food and drug administration experts when they change animals, from mice or rats to something else, after telling you that "rats . . . eat the same kinds of food we do and show the same effects of good and bad diet."

If there is anything that should succeed in breaking down the simple and childlike faith of the American mother and housewife in the trustworthiness of the food scientist and dietitian, it would be a brief examination of an important recent discovery. This revolutionary finding is to the effect that the customary and scientifically orthodox practice of feeding infants so that they might gain weight as rapidly as possible, is exactly *against* sound science. Experiments on rats (and this is one of the investigations which it would be of little use to *this* generation to try to do on men) showed that by *restricting* the diet of the young to fewer calories (without unbalancing it), a notable *increase in life span* is achieved; the rats underfed in infancy lived to nearly twice the age of the full-fed ones!

Full feeding of the young, which is a practical possibility in only about 13,000,000 of the whole population of the United States, on account of the planned privation basis of the Moley-Tugwell-Wallace-Roosevelt economy, evidently makes for shorter life. This theory has been tested upon rats and chickens, and upon animals still lower in the life scale, and in each case the animals that by frugal feeding are made to mature slowly had a much greater life span than the more rapidly growing ones. An up-and-coming drug advertiser has already made use of this important discovery to shout in large type, of the too-fat infant shown in his picture, MAYBE SO-O-O BIG IS *TOO* BIG, and in due time the baby food manufacturers and the baby experts and the pediatricians and diet advisers will be catching up with the enterprise of this drug firm and will hasten to assure you that they always did believe in babies that were a bit spare, or even skinny. Agricultural scientists, quick to turn to profit the results of nutritional science, are already at work making practical application of this method of increasing the life span of chickens. Perhaps it is not too much to hope that more studies may be made in time of the effect of this finding, applied to the more important but, for purposes of research, less highly regarded problems of human children.

It is interesting to note that what might be called the anthropological approach to the problem of diet which this book follows to a considerable extent as a test of diet adequacy and economic soundness, could have led scientists much earlier to the epochal finding that has just been presented. It is a matter of common knowledge, indeed, that nature does not penalize the race or the individual for a temporary failure of the supply of food or water. Poisons, like bad liquor, arsenic, or lead or ethyl (leaded) gasoline, may and usually do leave their permanent mark upon the organism and in some cases, as with arsenic and lead poisoning, horrible results may and do in fact appear twenty years or more after a farmer has been exposed to the insect sprays, or weed killer or sheep dip, or after a child or youth has taken the Fowler's solution of arsenic commonly prescribed by physicians to this day, as a tonic. But the after-penalty for poisoning comes because nature in the evolution of the race has had no occasion to make provision for correcting for the intake of poisons taken into the body regularly or daily as is now the case with nearly all who live under what we call civilized conditions. With the rarest exceptions, too insignificant for the processes of the cosmos to concern themselves with, poisons as we must face them now in a hundred forms and guises, were among primitive men simply not a factor in human environment, and the bodily organs made no adjustments to them, and did not develop special functions to dispose of them. But hunger and sexual deprivation, and wet, and cold short of freezing, and hot weather and dampness—all of these things had so important and inescapable a part in the life of many peoples in many places that it can be taken for granted that the mere fact of survival of individuals and their tribes was evidence of all needed adjustment of the body to the problem. Normally, when the organism survived, it did not carry a penalty for having been exposed to the vicissitude, any more than an animal which is for a long time without a mate loses the power of reproduction, or a puppy which is for a day or two unfed, is unable to recover fully when access to the food supply is again possible. It will appear again and again in this book that many diet problems of the utmost consequence are easily attacked by no more advanced or scientific tool than common sense. If common sense did not teach that a diet which is light, but adequate in kind and quality, was without permanently harmful effect on the body, Mr. Roosevelt and the relief administrations in every city and state would be carrying a larger burden of guilt for the future degradation and early demise of our American population than even politicians are accustomed to bear and to rationalize!

In calling attention to the discrepancy between their findings, in studies on rats, and the conventional assumption of nutritionists with respect to the desirability of rapid growth of children, a group of scientists at Cornell University stated: "Modern practice of nutrition applied in rearing both children and animals, assumes that the diet which produces the most rapid growth in the young is the best for assuring the optimum health and longevity of the adult." That is, longevity and maximum growth rate, science determines, when it gets around to the matter, are incompatible. Dr. Sherman of Columbia University, according to a *Science Service* release of September 30, 1933, held that the work of nutrition experts will "form a bulwark against disease, enlarge the prime of life, and postpone senility." Another nutrition worker, Dr. Agnes Fay Morgan of the University of California in July of 1933, also heralded the coming of vastly improved infant health and survival; lowered mortality and morbidity at all ages; *accelerated rates of growth in children;* and more comfortable as well as longer deferred and longer lasting old age. Among the triumphs of nutritional science she included as her third point one which the findings of Dr. McCay (of the Cornell scientists) show clearly to have been not a triumph but an error of the first magnitude. Indeed, "lowered mortality and morbidity" and "more comfortable as well as longer deferred and longer lasting old age" were strictly incompatible, so far as animal experiments are concerned (which are Dr. Morgan's favorite method of research on nutrition problems), with those very same "accelerated rates of growth in children"; yet to Dr. Morgan all were proofs of the high social value of research in nutrition.

It is natural that laboratory workers concerned with results which they can see and measure, and so bring within the ambit of their intellects, should have been carried away by the superficial advantage of rapid growth-rate. It was easy to measure, gave results that had the advantage of seeming positive and definite. Academic scientists love definite findings; unless their results can be expressed in tables, curves, and statistical graphs, with correlation coefficients, their fellow workers in the sciences are likely to hold that they have been thinking and developing mere "value-judgments" instead of working at their recognized routines and techniques. The latter tend to come out in the Alice-in-Wonderland form typified by the study, "Calcifying factors in the diet of Salamander Larvae," a masterpiece emanating from the University of Wisconsin, and often as not have little or nothing to do with physical and nutritional realities of men, women, and children).[1] On the whole it seems likely that the race will for a long time to come be better off if it depends for its guidance on food questions upon the common sense of persons who are far enough away from rat experiments that they can at least imagine a possible disadvantageous effect in later life from excessively rapid

[1] Other thesis titles which represent the work being done in the field of nutrition are the following: "Inorganic salts in Nutrition. . . ." "The mineral metabolism of rats receiving a diet low in inorganic constituents" (Yale University); "Some dietary factors concerned with the consumption and utilization of food in rats" (St. Louis University).

growth in infancy or can see that getting vitamin D along
with the poison or poisons in commercial cod liver oil may
be worse than getting too little of the vitamin. It is no
tribute to the abilities of nutrition scientists that they should
have, so to speak, stumbled over each other in their haste to
adopt the growth curve of rats as an index of the desirability of food combinations and method of feeding. Far too
many nutrition workers give no consideration to the human
race's *experience* on infants fed inadequate diets, and
the circumstances so well instanced in an editorial of the
Journal of the American Medical Association appearing a
few days before Dr. Morgan's happy but misleading an-
nouncement about the value of nutrition scientists' great
services to mankind. In this editorial the American Medical
Association commented on a paper of McCay which appeared
in *Science* in April of 1933, in which it had been shown
that rats of the nutrition laboratory of twenty years before,
"fed on the crude mixed diets of that period were reported
to be of slow growth, many of them not reaching full adult
size till the end of one year. Certain recorded groups of that
time, maturing slowly, showed an average life span of more
than three and one-half years. McCoy's [McCay's is meant]
rats of today, fed modern diets for accelerating nutrition,
reach full adult size before the end of the first six months
and live on an average for less than eighteen months. . . .
'No one has ever found it possible, however, [to devise a diet
that will give] both rapid growth with early attainment of
maturity and longevity.' "

The interpretation of all sorts of experiments, "proving"
the value to the organism of additions of milk to the diet,
the use of ultra-violet glass and lamps, and the feeding of
concentrated vitamin substances, was based on findings fol-

lowing the standard pattern that the use of the recommended material or food, or food concentrate, in feeding a certain number of children or animals, produced an increased growth rate. Yet as just noted this very occurrence that was interpreted as in itself favorable to the use of extra milk or ultra-violet glass, cod liver oil or viosterol or what not, was, in fact, against the welfare of the child or animal judged by its future expectation of life and health. And if there are any of the readers of this book who think that a plump and roly-poly infant or puppy is a more fortunate creature than a normally developing one that will live longer and be freer from disease, certainly no one can stop such a person from following the nutrition discoveries and pronouncements at Columbia and avoiding the disquieting findings of such careful workers as Dr. McCay.

The work of Dr. McCay and his Cornell group has been remarkable in that it has recently resulted in the promulgation of two findings of the highest significance that are of predominant importance only to consumers: that on the harm of excessively rapid growth rate of infants, and the almost equally important disclosure [1] on the grave potential dangers indicated in experiments on goats, rabbits, and guinea pigs of excessive or unneeded use of cod liver oil. Quoting from a summary in *Chemical Abstracts:* "Goats grew normally upon such diets for 2 or 3 months, after which they dropped dead suddenly. Post-mortem examination of these goats showed severe heart lesions and frequently lesions in the muscles of the legs. Guinea pigs and rabbits tended to

[1] See, on potential dangers, and known toxicity to certain animals of cod liver oil, the paper: *Synthetic Diets for Herbivora, With Special Reference to the Toxicity of Cod-Liver Oil*, L. L. Madsen, C. M. McCay, and L. A. Maynard.

develop lesions of the leg muscles in the course of a month when fed such diets. Many of the rabbit hearts had also undergone pathological changes. The cod-liver oil of the diet was partly responsible for producing these muscle lesions. Rabbits fed 2 to 3% of cod-liver oil in a synthetic diet died sooner than those fed only lard with no supplement of fat-soluble vitamins. . . . In all cases cod-liver oil was fed at levels frequently recommended for human consumption."

There is a large and growing literature on the toxicity of cod liver oil, a literature which has to a singular degree escaped attention in technical and medical journals in the United States, where it should have been almost a matter of weekly or monthly discussion. Indeed, there is available a bibliography running to 37 pages of medical and other findings respecting the toxicity of cod liver oil, but hardly more than one or two articles or brief digests in the journals widely read by physicians and nutrition and home-economics workers. There is a strong vested interest in cod liver oil as a dietary adjuvant for grown-ups, and especially for children and farm animals. Those who by their research tend to discourage the general use of cod liver oil and other accepted vitamin preparations will find themselves in the midst of very unpleasant controversy, which in the present generation of college presidents and deans, will do the researchers' academic careers no good.

It is in order that those who are not aware of the pressures which are at work in university circles should realize that the most rapid promotion and social and academic acceptance come through scientists whose studies tend to increase the salability of products, especially factory products, to increase the attractiveness of their labeling, or to expand the use of a trade-mark. The extent to which university en-

dowments and gifts of trees and Arabian horses and radio
sets (these are all actual cases of big-interest gifts to one
university) tend to flow either from magnates of banking
and trade who have a product or service to sell, or from publishers of individual newspapers, newspaper chains or household magazines that live and wax very rich by the advertising
that supports them, is little known outside the immediate
university community. There is in fact an astonishing amount
of pressure of very persuasive and unremitting character
that tends to drive nutrition workers into fields that increase some business man's or newspaper publisher's income,
and away from fields that might discourage the consumption
of cod liver oil or of foods such as dried apricots (that contain the poisonous sulphur dioxide) or apples of the Far
Western variety, distributed upon a national scale, that
regularly carry large residues of arsenic and lead sprays
used to combat orchard insects.

The current commercializing trends in the universities
make them especially agreeable places of work for food
scientists who whoop it up for irradiated milk, or vitamin D
bread, white bread, despoiled of vitamin B, cottonseed oil,
commercial mayonnaise, sulphured dried apricots; and by
their findings lessen the supply of good, honest, traditional
food. By favoring these and a dozen other ersatz foods, and
"protective foods" to accompany them, so that the combination becomes nutritionally tolerable, food scientists like
McCollum, Mendel, and Sherman have the obvious effect,
even in the cases where they are unaware of the economic
effect of their reasoning, of making the deficient substitutes
bring a better price in the market and more profits to their
exploiters. In openly fascist countries, as Italy and Ger-
many, this drive for substitute foods of poor nutritional

value is ever in evidence. In a number of American universities, particularly those which have notable big business leanings, this drive toward research justifying second-rate and third-rate food supplies is found more and more congenial. There is a definite relation to be seen between political reaction (tendency to favor the well-to-do and condone the exploitation of the poor) and the practice of defending unwholesome and deficient diets and diets which require "protective foods" such as milk and oranges to make them workable. Scientists genuinely interested in the well-being of the lower strata of our economic system would press to see them fed foods good enough to make quite unnecessary any intake of "protective foods." There is no more reason why man, eating the foods that could be available in an economic system favoring abundance, should need protective foods, than that a fox or rabbit should seek nutritional advice at Columbia or the University of California.

It may be that in time the academic credits now given at some western institutions for ping-pong and polo, will be extended to include a certain number of semester hours for each new and salable vitamin concentrate devised or publicized. There might even be credit for hustling off the campus extreme reds who believe in the Jeffersonian democracy, and do *not* believe in eating sulphured dried peaches. Now as the result of certain work of a leading nutrition researcher of California's Department of Household Science some dried fruit is misleadingly labeled: "Prepared with sulphur dioxide which keeps the natural vitamins in the fruit." Providing the information that helps a fruit packing business, to change a label with an unpleasant suggestion of chemical preservatives to one that stresses, as this new one does, the positive appeal of vitamin values is the sort of cooperation with industry that gets a university researcher ahead in his career. Millions of consumers lose in such a case, but rich state universities are run for industry and not for the consumers who send their boys and girls to college—and pay the bills.

XII

THE HOME-ECONOMISTS ADD TO THE CONFUSION

A large responsibility for the degeneration of American food supply and the arts of cookery must be laid at the door of home-economists, formerly called domestic science teachers; it is this group who are the teachers of the household arts and who to a considerable extent, set themselves up as school and community and rural experts in nutrition. It is partly or largely to the home-economists that we owe the unending succession of vogues for raisins, bran, spinach, raw carrots, breakfast cereals, milk, gelatine desserts, and bananas. During the depression one of the major functions of the home-economists has been to show how the unemployed and underprivileged can, if necessary, live on practically nothing a week. Many respected institutions have made this shameful contribution to public misinformation. The North Dakota Agricultural College at Fargo has, for example, recently shown that "the average family of eight in North Dakota can eat well on $9.59 a week." Eating well, in home-economics terms, consisted of the following menu:

Breakfast—tomato juice, farina, toast, peanut butter, cocoa.

Dinner—griddle cakes, brown sugar syrup, tomato sauce, cookies, tea.

Supper—canned beef, sauerkraut, mashed potatoes, Norwegian prune pudding, coffee.

The nearest to a luxury to which the poor under this home-economics guidance are to have access is *canned meat*. This dietary is surely dangerously overloaded with carbohydrates. The experimental method used to "test" it is one rather typical of home-economics work; the short-time test on eight students, lasting "a full week," has not the least significance in determining what can be eaten for a long period without harm to the present and the next generation by an under-privileged, half-starved family already suffering for months or years from grave nutritional deficiencies.

Many such "experiments" have been reported in newspapers owned by portly, well-fed business men, to show how little recipients of relief really require to keep alive till factories need hands again. Such studies are exactly in the class of that performed by the rich man who, donning a clean pair of overalls, finds out all about the poor by a Saturday afternoon visit to the dockyards; or a metropolitan newspaper reporter who understands the problem of the unemployed miner at first hand by a week-end trip, with cash in his pocket, to a Pennsylvania anthracite town.

Perhaps the greatest disservice of home-economists is that they have degraded our food supply through their contribution to and connection with advertising agencies, women's magazines, newspapers' women's pages, and the like, bringing about a general and rapidly growing substitution of dried, bottled, packaged, canned, and preserved, for fresh, savory, vitamin-containing food materials. To home-economists we are also indebted for the increasing substitution of color and appearance for quality and savor in foods. Home-economics texts, articles in magazines, and exhibits show amazing devotion to the beauties of form and arrangement of the

kitchen and table, the silverware and the napery, dishes of
strange color and form, "new" foods and new combinations,
to the uniforms worn by the waitress, to the chromatic and
statuesque attractiveness of the salads. These ideas are exploited again and again in writings of home-economists in
their professional journals and typify the present trend of
a vocation which finds the art and science of nutrition too
difficult or too humble. It delights to substitute the insub-
stantialities of glassware and linen, of sauces and garnishes
for the chemical and engineering realities of an honest food
supply; in place of competent cookery it would have: "dis-
plays of *tempting* cookies and candies and *dainty* linens
suitable for home entertaining." In speaking of textiles and
clothing it emphasizes "the relation of correct posture and
carriage to *beautiful and becoming dress,* while appropriate
design, *charming color,* and texture of fabrics were shown
by an assortment of carefully chosen textiles." In speaking
of a *nutrition* exhibit: "spotless furniture useful in an efficient kitchen, along with fresh, *crisp* vegetables, *brilliant*
fruits and other foodstuffs." [Italics mine.]

A dinner given by one of the women's magazines (the
Woman's Home Companion) to the home-economists assembled at the annual meeting of their national association
(American Home Economics Association) in 1934 was
termed in the *Journal of Home Economics* "a perfect meal."
This perfection was described as follows: "Hearts of celery,
radishes, green olives, and salted nuts were of course on the
table. The first course was *delicately molded crab flakes on
artichoke hearts.* This was followed by bortsch, the famous
Russian vegetable soup, with sour cream as a dressing and
tiny meat pastries as accompaniment. Then came fresh, hot

Kennibec [sic] salmon [1] served as was the turbot in the English dinner on a large platter, but with two accompaniments—one a well-blended tartar sauce served from *honey-dew melon baskets* and the other sliced cucumbers with an indescribably delicious *dressing.* The main course was breast of guinea, served with a *sauce of candied black cherries* and with green peas as the vegetable. The salad was of *pineapple and pimento cream cheese,* and the dessert *baked Alaska containing fresh strawberry ice cream and with fresh strawberries as a garnish.*" [Italics mine.] Following this description, the home-economist's *Journal* admits that the change from the traditional diet with "an over-abundance," as they describe it, "of fish, flesh, and fowl" has been brought about by a "gradual increase in knowledge of the composition and nutritive value of vegetables," that is, by home-economic learning and skills.

The surprisingly businesslike bias of the home-economist's learning and skills is nicely illustrated by a meeting of educators and economists discussing home-economics as a vital study. The leading speakers were a professor (whose special interest is in household finance and budgeting) at Teachers College, Columbia University's training school for home-economics teachers, New York City; a professor of *physical education* at Teachers College; a writer on the *Delineator* Magazine; Mrs. Emily Post, the etiquette expert; Katharine A. Fisher, the businesslike and aggressive head of Good

[1] That the waters of the Kennebec are now reported to be so polluted that the river no longer harbors salmon is a technical detail that would fail to interest home-economists even at "a perfect meal." Nor would it perhaps occur to them that at such a meal a special obligation applies to see that every detail of the food lives up to its description on the menu.

Housekeeping Institute, an advertising adjunct of Hearst's *Good Housekeeping Magazine;* and a writer of the *Ladies' Home Journal.* At a dinner which followed the meeting, leading speakers were *business* leaders, the head of the *Herald Tribune Magazine;* the head of the National Broadcasting Company; and the President of the Dime Savings Bank of Brooklyn.

At another convention of the American Home Economics Association than that mentioned a few paragraphs back there was a "bus trip to the Carnation Milk Company's interesting plant and then on to the famous Pabst Farm. Inspection of the dairies and factories at the first was followed by a picnic lunch, after which the busses carried the guests on to Oconomowoc where Mr. Pabst most hospitably arranged a horse race on his track, provided opportunity for bridge and swimming and all sorts of games, and finally served a typical Milwaukee-German supper to the whole crowd of several hundred and entertained them with German folk songs and dances by a well-known local club. . . . The busses left soon after breakfast to allow for a visit to the Brookfield Farm, home of famous sausages."

Home-economics women come away from commercial exhibits, "housekeeping institutes," and factory visits with their names registered on many mailing lists for advertising leaflets and "teaching and classroom material," and laden down with charts and booklets full of misleading and pseudo-scientific data in endless variety and varying degrees of implausibility. Such fraudulent and tricky literature forms a large part of the home-economists' teaching material, by which unknowing and helpless children are conditioned to the use not only of flavoring extracts, baking powder, root beer, tea, macaroni, and even a patent medicine iron tonic, but of

particular brands of such products, whose exploiters employ
a home-economics "educational" service for introducing such
material into the school system; and of every manner of
culinary imitation and abomination that infests *Good Housekeeping*, *Ladies' Home Journal*, the *Delineator*, *McCalls*,
Woman's Home Companion, and the rest of the organs of
housewife—and home-economist—miseducation.

The battle of margarine to remove consumer prejudice
was largely won by a leading home-economist, Ida Bailey
Allen, who, in each of six cities, "arranged a luncheon to
which were invited twenty-five or thirty of the city's key
women—society women, home-economics specialists, and
women's club leaders. All the food served was prepared with
Nucoa, and Nucoa was also supplied instead of butter as a
spread for bread. After the luncheon, Mrs. Allen arranged
for a demonstration and explanation of the uses of Nucoa
before an audience of from 500 to 1,500 local housewives.
The women who had eaten the food prepared with margarine
were unanimously enthusiastic. Some who had spread it on
their bread did not even realize they were not eating butter."
The phrase "unanimously enthusiastic" speaks for itself.
Home-economists, if they knew foods and were not merely
devotees of expensive and well-organized public dinners and
of organized campaigns to put over margarine, bananas,
milk, and ice cream, could not have been a part of the unani-
mous enthusiasm here described. Margarine may simulate
the flavor of butter so that home-economists not familiar
with butter and its properties could not tell the difference;
but margarine does not provide the essential food values that
are in butter, and its use simply rationalizes the introduction
of vitamins A and D into some other part of the food (or
medicine!) supply, as for example by way of cod-liver oil,

irradiated milk, irradiated yeast cakes, vitaminized cough drops, doped breakfast foods, and the like.

According to the American Restaurant Magazine, home-economists are featured in a modernization movement now gaining momentum among progressive restaurants. Modernization movements, be it known, are drives to get restaurant owners to buy the equipment advertised in trade journals, especially in the trade journal which boosts the modernization program. In this case, it was electrical equipment that was to be put over. "Competent home-economists prove that electric cookery is cool, clean, convenient, healthful and time-releasing." Home-economists who had, as all should have, a knowledge of the engineering factors underlying electric cookery, would also prove that electrical cookery is in most places expensive to install and to use, involves some elements of shock hazard to the user of the stove or range and has other noteworthy disadvantages which, with the present low quality of electric stoves, and at present customary rates for electricity and house wiring, make other cooking fuels more advantageous, *especially* for restaurants, to which the quoted item relates.

Editor & Publisher exhibits the commercialization of home-economics work in its description of the Home Management Institute of the *Alhambra* (Calif.) *Post-Advocate*. The newspaper Home Management Institute is, of course, a device for bringing in advertising, or as the oily phrase runs, "merchandising the newspaper and its service to the advertiser." Indeed, "one national advertiser who had completed his schedule without including the *Post-Advocate*, did a right-about-face after the project was outlined to him and ordered his current campaign into the Alhambra paper. . . . There will be a tie-in with this program to the home-economics class of the high school, by having it take charge of a certain number of programs." In Bridgeport "many stores are arranging for their own home-economists to be trained at Bridgeport in putting over an appliance cooking school as a means of stimulating interest in the often slighted small appliances." (*Retail Ledger*, December, 1934.)

The attitude and "availability" of home-economists could not be better illustrated than by the following quotations from *Electrical Merchandising*, March, 1934:

"Home-economics instructors at least are willing [to act as salesmen for electrical equipment]:

"I am interested in demonstrating electric refrigerators," says a home-economics teacher in Hoopeston, Illinois. "We have a number of home-economics graduates in Rockford, Illinois, who would be glad to do this sort of work," says another home-economics teacher of the school system of that city. "I should be very happy to assist in electrical refrigerator demonstrations on Saturdays and during the summer months," says a home-economics teacher in Hinckley, Illinois. Even the dean of a tax-supported state college is quoted as approving such demonstrations (selling talks) by home-economics teachers.

"The school teacher who demonstrates will do well to 'check' all big words and make clear to older women in the audience that they are doubtless better cooks than she is," declares Miss Nell M. Snavely, home-economist for R. Cooper, Jr., Chicago." The school teacher who does that will not only be employing a shrewd advertiser's tactic, she will also be telling what is rare indeed for domestic science teachers, the whole truth on an important topic!

One can well exemplify the curious want of any real technical content of home-economics training and practice that goes with this business-like activity by the example of one Miss Peacock who, in 1934, according to *Electric Refrigeration News* of Jan. 3, 1934, was appointed as a person well-qualified to head the home economics activities of the Kelvinator Corporation. After graduating from Iowa State College and teaching home economics at a preparatory school in Sioux Falls, S. Dak., and in Kansas City, she became *stylist* in the household linens department of Marshall Field & Company, and later the "educational director" (that is, it may be assumed, from a knowledge of what trade associations mean by "education," purveyor of ice-cream trade propaganda) of the Ice Cream Institute of Chicago. Her present activity will be in the holding of what are curiously termed "cooking schools" and in setting up *"home-economics departments* for Kelvinator distributors" and carrying on research in the "relationship between modern electric refrigeration and efficient home management."

The Home Economics Department of the Southern Rice Milling Industry offers to home-economics teachers material prepared under the direction of a home-economist with a Master of Science degree, with experience in high school and college teaching, as a state extension worker, and as a demonstrator and lecturer. This material includes The Rice Cook Book, which is not merely a brief for rice but a brief for Southern grown rice, alleged to have superior cooking qualities. Such a pronouncement is of course not a scholarly work on the subject suitable for promulgation by a university, yet it was prepared by the Home Economics Department of Louisiana State University. There are besides The Story of Rice—From seed to table; A rice wall chart for schools; Rice in the Nursery School, by an Iowa State College assistant professor of child nutrition; Rice in the Hospital, by the head dietitian, Cook County Hospital, Chicago. Since the commonly-sold milled white rice is devoid of vitamin and mineral substances, which are removed from rice, as they are from wheat in the milling of white flour, with the bran coating of the grain, it is hard to see just how home-economics and nutrition teachers of a reputable university could consider a contribution to sales-propaganda for so badly degraded a foodstuff properly in line with their teaching duties. Milled white rice, indeed, perhaps excels all other common foods as an example of profitable denudation of an important foodstuff in a fashion that renders it substantially unfit for human consumption. As in the case of white bread, the rice millers argue for their product by holding in effect that if you eat a variety of other *good* foods with it, such as eggs, fruits, vegetables, and meats, it will do you no harm— which is a roundabout way of putting rice and white flour in the class of sugar, candy, and cottonseed oil.

"Every Home Economist," says an advertisement in the official *Journal of Home Economics*, ". . . should know about the marvelous new way of making *real* ice cream with Burnett's READY-MIX. . . . *Delicious* because it contains Burnett's Pure Vanilla; always factory fresh because it's wrapped in CELLOPHANE. . . . It's real news for class projects, too!" Others than home-economists have discovered that products wrapped in cellophane often *need* extra attractiveness to assure their salability and that ready-mixed ice cream is about the last thing that a qualified home-economist would use for "class projects," if she had due respect for her art, the art of pedagogy, and the future economic and nutritional life of the children in her classes. The Home Economics Department E-6, of the Kellogg Company at Battle Creek, Mich., in an advertisement on the same page

considers *Rice Krispies* and fresh fruit a delicious warm
weather dish. "These tempting, toasted bubbles . . . snap,
crackle and pop with nourishment and goodness." A little
more training in physics on the part of home-economists and
another explanation than "nourishment and goodness" might
have been necessary to account for the snapping, crackling,
and popping in this advertisement. The same advertisement
in the *Journal of Home Economics* includes a way of using
Rice Krispies in making stuffed peppers with cooked ground
ham and cooked ground pork. "Visit our booth at the Home
Economics Convention and receive other recipes and suggestions for using cereals." Business men may, and do, think
this a proper way for recipes to be originated, but the
parent of the home-economics organs of the country could
reasonably be expected to know better and surer ways for
arriving at genuine contributions to the culinary arts.

A university hospital dietitian in a radio talk announced
that "with mechanical refrigeration fresh vegetables will
keep a number of days"! It is a fact, however, that without
mechanical refrigeration, but with a proper, old-fashioned
storage place, farmers and small town folk for centuries
have kept fresh vegetables a number of months. "Canned
foods are well graded," says the same woman. "Every food
company carries brands that indicate grades." This is a
totally incorrect statement and gravely misleading to this
woman's listeners, and a person really qualified in food supply problems would have known it was not true. In continuing her discussion, this "food expert" failed entirely to point
out that the basis for *commercial* grading of canned fruit is
altogether irrelevant to a *proper* (consumer-oriented) basis
of grading of canned fruit. Proper grading would not give,
as commercial grading does, a high grade to excessive sweet-

ness and accidental and nutritionally insignificant characteristics such as uniformity of size and color, but would rate
highest those qualities which are most characteristically lacking in nearly all commercially canned foods. All or nearly all
commercial grading gives favorable weight to those very
characteristics which are least desirable from the standpoint
of human nutrition. The best canned peaches, for example,
from the commercial grader's point of view, endorsed by the
dietitian just quoted, are those which show the most durability and uniformity of texture and color in the can. Commercially canned peaches must stand a great deal of rough
handling and abuse and a high grade is given to those types
whose appearance and texture will stand up after a long
period of shipment in jolting freight cars, jarring and
bouncing trucks and long periods of standing in the hot sun
in the freight yard or on the freight house or warehouse
platform. Another highly regarded characteristic of canned
fruits from the point of view of the *commercial* grades
assigned to them is high sugar content of the syrup, which
again is exactly the opposite of the characteristic which
would be most desirable physiologically and from the consumer's point of view. Over-sweet canned fruits are as undesirable for consumers' alimentary tracts as would be over-
eating of candy or three teaspoonfuls of sugar in a cup of
coffee. Really fine, ripe, and mellow fruits are not canned
commercially; or if they are they are very likely to be given
a low or even substandard grading, by the trade and by the
government grading experts.

A lack of knowledge of fundamental problems of physiology and nutrition is characteristic of home-economists and
other unqualified groups, all too well exemplified by the case
just cited of a completely false but generally accepted basis

for grading of canned foods. Dr. W. W. Bauer, writing in *The American Mercury*, October, 1934, said of home-economic science: "The human digestive system is not built on the bovine model, and cannot handle roughage in the same manner. Diet faddists have something to answer for in the American addiction to diets that are rough and tough on the colon." This criticism of course relates directly to the excessive roughage in the American diet mainly caused by home-economic teaching which promotes the extensive misuse of spinach, bran, raw cabbage, cauliflower, berries, pineapple, and citrus fruits dear to the ladies who have so recently been indoctrinated with ideas about roughage and assorted vitamins from A to G, and especially persuaded of the overwhelming significance of the vitamin C (admittedly essential to the health and welfare of that peculiar tropical animal, the guinea pig). It will be but a short step from the grading of canned goods on the basis most satisfactory to the canners, to the grading of layer cake on a basis most suitable to the requirements of commercial bakers whose problem it is, just as with the fruit and vegetable canners, to produce a product distinguished for its structural strength, resistance and long lasting qualities.

The *Journal of Home Economics* so far forgets its functions as the organ of a quasi-scientific or at least craft organization as to discuss the value of well-selected advertising techniques in selling foods to children in the school lunch room. "Often a well-selected adjective has helped to sell an only moderately popular dish. For instance, 'green apple pie' appeals much more than just straight 'apple pie,' and 'oyster stew with crispy crackers' seems more alluring than 'oyster stew with crackers.' One manager who became much interested in this phase of lunch-room work found that when

she gave a certain kind of chocolate cake the amusing name
of Weary Willie, its sales increased almost fifty per cent."
To expect teachers of young children and children in the
high school to succeed in inculcating the faintest adumbra-
tion of the scientific method or anything significant in respect to the use and development of ideas is to expect too
much when this type of toying with adjectives, as a means
of selling foods, and foods in part undesirable for children,
so deeply permeates the thinking of the workers in the home-
economics vineyard. Home-economics with that kind of a
slant is not even a respectable trade like cobbling or well-
digging; it is a business—one of the less respectable forms
of merchandising. If it be true that in our present economic
order it is necessary to make salesmen universally out of
children, then the home-economics teacher who offers apples
as green apple pie is following a method proper to business
—to a candy-kitchen or soda fountain. It is not, however,
a method which will make consumers believe that home-
economists know foods or children's digestions or have professional or craft integrity.

The *Journal of Home Economics* reported a comparison
of commercial and homemade food mixes which included
ready-mixed pancakes, gelatin, chocolate pudding, and biscuits; but the researcher based the comparison upon foods
prepared by a "college trained student who had not had a
great deal of practical experience;" in other words, a home-
economics student rather than a cook. The conclusion quite
naturally followed: "hence in most cases the homemade products were to be rated good, but not outstanding." The judging of the products was done "by a group of six who graded
appearance, flavor, and texture on a carefully worked out
score card." Nothing is said in the report as to any one or

more of the six being a qualified cook or chef whose training and experience would make her judgment of commercial versus homemade mixes worth the price of the paper on which the score card was mimeographed. The method used was as appropriate as would be the rating of a hospital by a plebiscite of a radio audience, or of a surgical instrument by a vote of freshman medical students. Only a home-economist or an advertising agency could think of comparing foods upon the judgment of persons quite lacking in food preparation skills of a high order, and only a word-minded editor who was herself far out of touch with skills and scientific method alike, could have passed such a report for printing in the official *Journal of Home Economics,* as in the least relevant to the central problem of home economis as potentially the most important of all the useful arts.

The fact that something over 30 per cent of the Home Economics Association's total receipts come from advertising gives it much the same problem in this field as the American Medical Association (which gets more than *half* of its annual income from business sources). At the annual meeting of the Home Economics Association, the commercialization which surrounded the exhibits permeated the whole policy and management of the meeting; one feature of the meetings was the issuance during the sessions of a sort of commercial daily newspaper devoted to publicity and advertising; for this paper, as it turned out later, the Association would accept no official responsibility, though its distribution and the indoctrination it provided were an important element of the sessions. Though the question of commercial domination of the Association has been much under discussion in its inner circles in recent times (though never appearing in its publications), nothing much can be done about the alarming situation since so large a proportion of the Association's support and membership comes from business interests accustomed to use home-economists' prestige and quasi-professional standing as a means of exploiting their products. Especially significant in this connection is the extent to which the home-economists, connected with the women's magazines which are predominantly organized for advertising, exercise an important degree of control in the functioning of the national and regional home-economics associations. Any shift of policy of the association in the direction of professionalizing its practices and de-commercializing its meetings and journals, would be met by big business interests in the food and household appliance fields by a quick shut-down on financial support of the national association and its state and regional affiliates. Withdrawal of a few full page advertisements for dessert gelatine and baking powder and commercial baker's goods would do the trick quite easily and cheaply.

Even in the high schools and other schools in small towns, enormous emphasis is given the gadgetry of the kitchen and especially to the appearance of foods, and none or almost none to the values inherent in traditional cookery, in the part which trial and error over hundreds or thousands of years have played in determining cooking methods and formulas, in determining valuable food combinations, or to the questions of instinct and occupational and cultural patterns and the age and type of a civilization in determining one's choice of food.

Home-economics teachers are always found as ready to help out in a commercial exploitation as office boys are to attend a ball-game. A representative of a gas company, as reported in *Editor & Publisher* of November 3, 1934, said that gas modernization programs can advantageously be introduced by the "heads of home-economics departments of colleges, and members of the staffs of magazines and newspapers." A Mr. Steinmetz who was quoted in this connection, said such people "are glad to cooperate and permit the use of their names." But Fleischmann's Yeast has to go abroad to get medical testimonials for its product, and even cosmetic advertisers have to do their testimonial getting largely among the minor nobilities and the "beerage," and advertising agencies have little luck in landing their 4-color cigarette-smoking ladies from among the educated classes who have college degrees and academic positions. Why must home-economics teachers be such outstanding fall-girls for trade, when teachers of French and oil-painting require larger and more impressive inducements?

The India Tea Bureau of New York has a "Home Economics Division" which promotes increased consumption of tea by sending lecturers throughout the country, who talk to housewives not on the increased consumption of tea but on "The Hospitality of the Tea Table." Increased consumption is the expected by-product of the lectures, and the housewives who think about such matters will have one more reason for associating home-economists with the shrewd and roundabout techniques and trickeries of advertising men.

The close tie even of research in the home-economic field to big business is illustrated, and typically, by the authors of a paper on "Tenderness and Juiciness of Cooked Meat," who in a footnote in the *Journal of Home Economics*, "express their thanks to the National Live Stock and Meat Board for a grant [to the University of Chicago] which helped defray expenses of this work; and to Dr. C. R. Moulton of the Institute of American Meat Packers for helpful suggestions." The home-economics department at the University of California has done notable services for the dried fruit industry of that state, in devising scientific-sounding reasons why sulphuring of the fruit is good rather than bad for the stomach. On the other hand, the home-economics department in this university is rather distinguished for the little it has done and the few publications it has issued for the use and benefit of the consumers of California and other states.

When home-economic research is not outrageously commercial, it is, as Gretta Palmer put it in the *New York World-Telegram*, likely to be:

"Much Ado About Nothing.

"Home economics students have recently devoted their efforts to such burning topics as 'Photographic Studies of Boiled Icing,' which won a Master of Arts degree from the University of Chicago, and 'The Relation of Maturity, Size, Period in Storage and Variety to the Speed and Evenness of Cooking in Potatoes,' which significant investigation was conducted at the University of Maine. There is also the fascinating brochure on 'Factors Controlling Internal Temperatures of Butter Cakes During Baking,' compiled by two young women at the University of Nebraska.

"If trained research students who are spending the taxpayers' money in State universities devote their time to such problems as these it is not surprising that the average housewife runs amuck when she tries to budget her leisure time. Her contributions to civilized thought could hardly be less than those made by our bespectacled Doctors of the Philosophy of baked potatoes."

The most complete sell-out of home-economics integrity that has come to notice so far is that of the "Educational Department" of the National Confectioners' Association whose job it is to break down candy clichés such as "tooth decay is caused by candy" and "candy is fattening." The industry, through its "Educational Department," sends out stories to the newspapers and to the Associated Press, which are allegedly used by newspapers over the entire country. The "Educational Department" has a serious problem in striving to overcome the "feminine misconception of candy as an enemy of the slim figure. . . . Stories are released of athletes and actresses who eat candy for the quick energy it supplies without adding weight. [A downright falsehood, of course.] For instance, a picture of a popular motion picture star eating candy, and one who is distinctive for her beautiful and slim figure, will soon be sent to newspapers from coast to coast. The accompanying story will point out that this lovely creature is able to endure the long hours of strenuous work on the movie lot because she munches candy frequently.

"One of the large movie companies provided the photograph, and this department will release it and the story in matrix form to the one thousand newspapers who continually print our publicity."

One of the jobs of the publicity department of the candy manufacturers is to stop unfavorable or adverse criticism. A great insurance company was called off from continuing to print a perfectly true statement which it made in a booklet about diet, with respect to the unwisdom of eating candy between meals.

Now come the candy home-economists: "In the past few months the Publicity Department covered candy in the school cafeteria for *Practical Home Economics,* a publication which extends practical help in teaching foods to Home Economics Teachers, School Cafeteria Managers, and others. The circulation totals over 16,000. This article pointed out various ways of achieving an attractive display of candies in the school cafeteria and stressed the nutritive properties of candy as a food essential in the diet of school children." Candy is *not* ever, or in any amount, a food essential in the diet of school children. It is as far from being such an essential as any material one could name, possibly, except *Coca Cola* or coffee-cognac or anchovy-paste. The putting over of candy for school lunchrooms and in other ways among teachers of young children and among the children themselves is as shady and dishonest and nutritionally menacing an enterprise as anyone has conducted in these states in many a year. In a country where the use of sugar runs to ten or twenty times the amount that should be consumed, to inculcate *greater* use of sugar among children who can least well tolerate it without grave danger to teeth and general health and freedom from disease, is morally on a par with teaching babies to use cosmetics and aspirin, or workingmen to go in for absinthe. But a moral sense on such matters goes, when it is found at all, only with craft skills and scientific knowledge, and few besides home-economists will allege that the leaders and journals in the home-economics field have either in significant amount.

Another food and health magazine for which the candy-home-economist writes with the home-economics point of view is the *Forecast.* "Intriguing table decorations composed of candy were suggested for the luncheon, bridge, and dinner table" in an article in this magazine. Proving perhaps that the reading matter you get for a low price through the "courtesy" of advertisers is worth even less than is paid for it.

Such monstrosities as peppermint ice cream, made, of course, not out of peppermint but out of peppermint candy, are put over by this "educational department" of the candy manufacturers. "Chocolate Center Rolls" was, according to the story in the candy trade journal from which this information is taken, another instant " 'hit' with the editors of home-economics departments" (presumably of the daily newspapers). This recipe, which "had a Continental background" happened, in the United States, to require the use not merely of chocolate, but of a chocolate candy bar. It was reprinted in 65 newspapers, including the *Chicago Tribune*, which included it on the first page of its Sunday Women's Feature Section, largely devoted to so-called home-economic subject matter, attaining a circulation of over 1,200,000. A recipe for cinnamon ice cream, a "delicious dessert" made not with cinnamon but with red cinnamon candies, appeared in 137 newspapers, including the *Newark News, Los Angeles Times, Ft. Worth Star Telegram,* and the *New York American,* all with large circulations. And to examine in turn the home-economics backgrounds of the newspaper women's pages: The former "food editor of the *Chicago Tribune,*" a trained home-economist who had done postgraduate work, was a teacher of home-economics for eleven years. She is now director of the cooking staff of the "Household Science Institute" (which isn't an Institute in the noncommercial use of that word), to which position she arrived after commercial work for the Evaporated Milk "Institute" and some of the larger meat packers. "She has given many years of study" to "gravy—which has long been a problem in institutional cooking."

The hardened publicity workers busily increasing the consumption of candy by children who are already consuming far and away too much of a product that is bad, both as a type of food and as to the particular practices of its manufacturers as to ingredients and methods of production, "find that school teachers are eager to include knowledge of candy along with the three r's, as indicated by the volume of letters received asking for any material available imparting this information. 'The Story of Candy,' a comprehensive and fascinating book written by Walter C. Hughes, and Dr. Bundeson's [1] 'New Knowledge of Candy' are constantly being mailed for educational purposes. To date copies of these booklets have been placed in the hands of 600,000 people." Home-economists and home-economics teachers are among the principal and most sought after users and disseminators of this type of material. Of course they cannot be expected to exhibit the critical judgment that would enable them to apply the necessary heavy discount to the candy-pronouncements of a Chicago Health Commissioner and a Senior Surgeon of the U. S. Public Health Service. It would take more than a home-economist's background to plumb the exact degree of propaganda in the utterances of so noted, honored, and eminent a public man.

The work of the candy men's "educational department" will only be completed, says the article from which this material is taken, "when women no longer shrink from a proffered piece of chocolate candy, when mothers no longer believe that candy is bad for their children, when false state-

[1] Dr. Bundeson is a professorial lecturer on public health at the University of Chicago, has been a vice-president and later president of the American Public Health Association, is senior surgeon of the U. S. Public Health Service with the rank of Lieutenant Colonel, and has for nine years been head of Chicago's public health administration.

ments cease to be written about candy." That is, to put it in a more candid and less candied fashion, when women have been completely bereft of reason and common sense about diet, when mothers have read enough newspapers and magazines that they cease to know what is safe for children to eat, and when the truthful and unfavorable criticisms of candy have finally been scared or squeezed out of all the newspapers and magazines and trade journals and school and college text books.

"Drink a Banana. . . . Introduce Banana Milk Shake to your classes" says an advertisement in the *Journal of Home Economics. "It has a real nutrition story."* (Italics mine.) Not only that, which shows what passes among nutrition teachers for nutritional science, but the "new Banana Milk Shake" which "is the talk of the town" as the advertisement puts it, was *"demonstrated* at the Home Economics Association convention."

Boys and girls and grownups are being taught by commercially indoctrinated teachers of home-economics and dietetics who graduate from Columbia, Chicago, and other great institutions, that life cannot be conducted on a satisfactory plane without mechanical refrigerators, electric stoves, and power driven drink-mixers and egg beaters.

The Georgia Power Company and many of the larger electrical utilities use home-economists to "build up residence load," which means in consumer English to sell consumers more electricity. The official organ of the home-economists (*Journal of Home Economics*, May 1933), far from deprecating the encroachments of utilities upon the school system, reports approvingly on the introduction of utility companies' "business methods, policies, and ethics" into the home economics training at Iowa State College. Indeed, special mention is made of the loss to the *companies* if the girls who will later tout electric refrigerators and waffle irons must go through an apprenticeship of six to nine months to learn "business practices," and to develop "keen business sense." Part of the students' training was "observing" the psychology of selling and [the appliance salesman's] methods in handling people," in calls and follow-up visits upon 75 housewives at Ames, Iowa. With the co-operation of two newspapers, even newspaper columns and articles (publicity for electric appliances), and advertising, and radio broadcasting are provided for. This is but another of the countless instances where the state university functions to help not the *people*, but the *business* of the state, and especially the business of selling. Without granting for a moment the right of the utility businesses to sell refrigerators by the devious methods described in this article, one can say without possibility of rebuttal that they have no right to train home-economists in so shady an art at the expense of the consumers of Iowa and in an institution which consumers' taxes have paid for. The people, as distinguished from the business firms of Iowa, might very reasonably resent the turning of the State's property and paid educators over to the narrow commercial interests of electric appliance companies and their shrewd tacticians of the sales force.

The home service director of the Peoples Gas Company, of Chicago, speaking on "Fashions in Food" to restaurant men, puts very clearly the position of the home-economist as a hand maiden of business enterprise: ". . . You can profit by having as dietitian a *home-economics trained woman* who intelligently understands that she must pay her own salary and make a profit besides. *A woman knows how to economize and make a showing with a dab of this and that, as a piece*

of tomato or orange. When peas are thirty cents a pound
serve buttered cabbage and peas. *The sprinkling of six or
eight peas on the buttered cabbage is very effective and a
pound goes a long way.* . . . Did you ever hear of a *mineral cocktail*—water vegetables have been boiled in, strained,
cooled, served with slice of lemon? . . . *I get a good
'chicken' salad off a pork (not veal) loin.*" [Italics mine.]
Home-economics training and performance that result in
attitudes of this type toward consumers will be difficult to
reconcile to with the view that some profess to hold, that
economics and home-economics teaching are semi-profes-
sional in character.

The Home Economics in Business department of the
American Home Economics Association represents in a
well-organized, high-pressure fashion, the point of view
which these activities typify. This business wing of the domestic science group prepared an exhibit of "educational
material" put out by commercial firms *which is to be at the
disposal of State Home Economics Associations.*

The association, that is, not only accepts advertising and
propaganda material of a great group of commercial, profit-
making manufacturers and processors, but uncritically takes
over even their grossly misleading "educational material."
"Educational material" is of course the term used to justify
introduction of commercial advertising into school rooms
where the child is supposed to be protected from commercial
propaganda of profit-business.

Propaganda for a different and decent social order where
the drive for adulterated bread and for putting candy over
on helpless children would quickly atrophy from weakening
of the motivation, is held to be an improper activity for a
school teacher; and the majority of the teachers themselves

supinely accept and even rationalize as justifiable, the pro-
hibition set down by business-men-trustees and school boards
against "radical propaganda" for a society motivated by
the instinct of sound workmanship, social service and production for use. But no teachers find it important or even
expedient to fight openly against the reactionary and dishonest propaganda for excessive use of cereals, milk, ice
cream, cocoa, candy, or orange and tomato juice in the
school lunch and in the child's meals at home.

The isolated teacher of home-economics gets an enormous
amount of free educational material. One agency, the Home
Makers' Educational Service, is set up to provide her with
a regular service of commercial advertising material and
samples of advertised kitchen and household products, furnished "free" to a large mailing list by such firms as the
makers of *Burnett's* flavoring extracts, *Rumford Baking
Powder*, *India* tea, *Mueller's* macaroni products, *Bon Ami*,
Resinol soap and ointment, *Zonite* antiseptic and ointment,
Forhan's Tooth Paste, and *Pequot* sheets. This service offered to its advertisers a consumer coverage of 12,000 home-
economics teachers, 2870 home demonstration agents (who,
being government employees should be getting their teaching
material from a source at least as non-commercial as the
Federal government), and a total of 1,000,000 high school
and college students and 1,200,000 housewives. The individual manufacturer paid from $6,000 to $9,000 for the
service of having his product thus surreptitiously introduced
into the school system. The teacher is almost never allotted
funds to buy or prepare honest and competent and disinterested charts showing sources of carbohydrates, protein,
minerals, vitamins; and various other useful diagrams,
tables, pictures, etc., for educational purposes. As in her

characteristic timidity she does not dare ask for such funds, she falls a ready victim to General Food Factories, International Super-Preserves, Consolidated Grape-Fruit growers or whatever prosperous firm or trade association it is that has a lot of such things to give away free at the moment in consideration of the indoctrination of young children and high school students, with the idea that somebody's bran flakes or *Soupquick* or peppermint ice cream is a fine, essential food product.

The difficult position of the association of home-economics teachers and commercial food and appliance demonstrators and nutrition researchers arises mainly in the fact that its members do not see themselves as qualified technicians, but rather as teachers or coordinators of something or other, vaguely summed up in such terms as the family and its relationships, clothing appreciation, family economics, budget planning, flower arrangements, and decoration of the home. Absurd though it seems, emphasis on consumers' problems is one of the newer aspects of home-economics and one which is resisted by home-economics teachers and others in the profession. The first reason for this resistance is that emphasis on consumers goods and their qualities is bound to bring its practitioners into continuous and dangerous conflict with commercial interests and their mighty and ubiquitous propaganda machine for bread, bran, sugar, candy and baking powder, oranges, process cheese, and canned goods. A second reason is that close concern with consumers' problems involves detailed personal knowledge and some degree of skill in qualitative and quantitative chemical analysis, engineering design, methods of test of household appliances from vacuum cleaners to can-openers, nutritional science (*not* dietetics!), testing of materials,

textile analysis, biochemistry, bacteriology, and a score of
other sciences and technical arts in which one must *know*
what one is talking about in order to be able to maintain
professional standing and reasonable immunity to criticism
among the regular practitioners of these arts and sciences.
The rules for admittance to the profession, so called, of
home-economics are so liberal as to exclude practically no
one who professes an interest in the vague and unformu-
lated aims and purposes, mainly pseudo-sociological, of
home-economists. There is no professional qualification of
home-economists in the sense in which the term is used by
entomologists, chemists, pathologists, mechanical engineers,
physicists, and other technicians in their respective profes-
sions and professional societies. Competent professionals
know and can tell you what a civil or mechanical or sanitary
engineer should know to be able competently to practice his
profession. No home-economist can tell you in the same con-
crete, well-formulated way what constitutes a professional
home-economist's theoretical knowledge and skills.

The planlessness and de-professionalizing of the household arts is well illustrated by the following from the *Journal of the National Education Association,* from the pen of
the president of the American Home Economics Association:

"Home-economics was once a technical subject dealing
mainly with the preparation and use of household com-
modities and with the care and operation of household
equipment, but the philosophy which devoted major emphasis to practical skills is no longer in harmony with
present modes of living. New values have been introduced
into homemaking as many of the former functions of the

family have been taken over by industry and other agencies in the community."

The author almost succeeded in summing up in this brief paragraph the futility and economic naïveté of present day home-economics teaching. She did not note at all the irretrievable social loss involved in the declining interest of home workers and home-economics teachers in the household arts and skills, with which has gone a complete failure to apply critical judgment to the *quality of the functioning* of "industry and other agencies in the community" with respect to the functions of the family and of homemaking that have been taken over and become a part of profit business.

Many have suggested that home-economists should ally themselves directly with consumers and try to bring about a definite advocacy of consumers' rights exactly equivalent in directness and vigor to the demands made by other groups on behalf of labor, capital, railways, farmers, in governmental and educational affairs. But so far as home-economists are concerned, consumers have been left pretty much without defense or aid; the latters' alliance has been more consistently with business, with business-allied "Institutes" of Household Science and with the more business-minded aspects of education, than with those who as purchasers of goods provide the money for *Ladies' Home Journal* advertising and for the dividends of industry. Though this writer has read home-economics journals and bulletins for years, he has yet to see a discussion in one of them by a home-economist who gives up for a time being thrilled by the rich and delicious goodness and vitamin values of oranges, pears, and tomatoes, and warns of the dangers of the artificial ripening methods used for these fruits; or denounces the arsenic and lead poisoning inherent in the ordinary uninstructed use of them, especially in respect to the growing use of grated rind of citrus fruits in cakes, candies, and desserts. If there are exceptions to this rule, they are so rare and would apply in such limited sense, as not to warrant special treatment. To expect help for consumers from the generalty of home-economists is about as reasonable as to look to the great investment bankers and insurance companies to give up their well-organized exploitation of farmers and factory workers. Home-economists in the field of foods and food preparation equipment are humble workers in the gardens of all those businesses that sell a low-cost product at a fancy price, from colored oranges, pancake flour and packaged cornstarch dessert, to electric cooking appliances, washing machines, and mechanical refrigerators.

XIII

THE MILK FAD—MAN A PARASITE UPON THE COW

For all of the tremendous ballyhoo which supports the consumption of milk in this country by young and old, it is difficult to find any but the most insubstantial scientific support. Milk, so far as can be judged from the material now in hand, is, as to its place in the American diet, in exactly the category with bran—one of those things which was put over by ingenious and plausible advertising and salesmanship, in which were involved scores of expert publicity and advertising men, thousands of writers for magazines, nearly all of the high school and college teachers of home-economics and dietetics, many health officers, and worst of all, nearly all of the teachers of nutritional science. Often it happens that the very simple considerations which would suffice to determine the probable truth of a supposedly scientific finding are entirely ignored and conclusions reached upon very elaborate and hazily reasoned considerations which can be broken down by a very simple and elementary line of questioning. Indeed, common sense should indicate that the great vogue for milk which has resulted in nation- and state-wide propaganda campaigns for its increased consumption must be based upon some pretty flimsy evidence. The State of New York, for example, which recently appropriated the sum of $500,000 to increase milk consumption, of course on the ground of the public interest, sends out an endless flow of publicity and paid advertising "proving" that cow's milk is both a necessary food and a cheap food. Neither claim is true. Another claim is that it clears up the complexion. (Because in many cases milk is badly digested, it may make a bad complexion worse.) The State of New York, too, follows the ethics and intellectual élan established by General Mills in its *Vitality* booklet by calling upon movie stars and fiction writers for endorsement of milk as a reducing medicine. Quite the neatest trick of milk advertising is the State's advice that it be used as a food for those who wish to reduce, whereas everybody knows it was and is often prescribed by physicians as a food for those who wish to take on weight. Neither is it true as asserted by the great Doctors of Nutrition, McCollum and Sherman, publicized by New York State's Department of Agriculture, that milk is a " 'Protective Food' because it has a 'definite disease resisting' power and promotes vigorous buoyant health."

The American Public Health Association is quoted by the State of New York as saying: "Milk is called a 'protective food' because it makes up for many of the deficiencies of our civilized diet.

"Milk is of value in building sound teeth and strong bones, with its minerals, phosphorus and calcium. Milk supplies complete protein.

"Milk is an important source of vitamins—those mysterious things so necessary to growth and health. . . .

"How does milk acquire these wonderful health promoting properties? The answer points to green growing things, such as grass, grains, fruits and vegetables."

This ballyhoo for milk is open to exactly the same criticism that the American Medical Association rightly makes of "health food" advertising in that the claims for milk but emphasize those characteristics which are true of nearly all desirable food products, from boiled carrots to sirloin steak. Milk advertising is open to a further objection which the Medical Association committee on foods finds so potent in connection with other food products—the general vagueness about vitamins. Which vitamins are they of which milk is an important source? Milk as distributed in its recommended, pasteurized form is not an important source of two of the more important vitamins. The milk advertisers and the New York State publicity for milk conveniently forget the losses of vitamins which come about through improper, highly artificial feeding and housing of the cow and the heat treatment of the milk in the pasteurization process. As to the "disease resisting" characteristic referred to by Dr. Mc-Collum, carrots, vegetable soup, potatoes, meat, eggs, and fish all have disease resisting characteristics in exactly the sense in which Dr. McCollum must use the words of milk.

Why all this expensive and exceedingly respectable to-do about milk? In the first place, milk is especially subject to monopoly control, that is, is especially available for making money for people who already have a great deal, because health laws and ordinances have been and still are being manipulated in such form as to give a great advantage to the large-scale producer. The farmer used to bring his milk to town in a little one-horse wagon where he delivered to a few faithful customers who knew his ethics and honesty and his personal habits. The farmer-dealer pouring from his spout-can into the housewife's crock or jar does not fit into the present scheme of large-scale distribution because there is no way of making this process pay toll to Borden's, Sheffield, National Dairy Products, Dairymen's League, and the rest. It was in order, therefore, to introduce to the public mind by an endless stream of propaganda, and through the laws and ordinances of states and cities the idea of pasteurizing plants, whereby the little farmer and the small milk distributor would have to give way to business firms who could afford the large plant investment in machinery and buildings and working capital under the new regime of milk pasteurization. Pasteurized milk is safer than unpasteurized milk, but it is also by a fortunate coincidence a guaranty of monopoly profits to the large milk distributor. The shift of consumers to pasteurized milk turns the small farmer from a dealer in his own milk, cream, cheese and butter, making direct contact with his customers, into a seller of raw materials to a manufacturing business. This puts him at a permanent and overwhelming disadvantage financially and throws all of the advantages into the hands of those who own the trucks, the assembling plants, the pasteurizing plants, the bottling machinery, the by-product equipment for making casein, process cheese, acidophilus milk, butter, ice cream, dried skim milk, evaporated and condensed milk, and plastic cream (one of the many new and highly artificial milk products for commercial bakers' use). Those who can afford to hire the chemists, college professors of agricultural economics, and the lawyers to keep milk manufacture and distribution in its most profitable form, will continue to own the plants and equipment and control the prices paid to farmers, until the farmer and consumer together rebel at the exploitation and make milk production and distribution into a state function.

As to the supposed superior health values of milk, it is a fact that milk is very indigestible for a considerable number of people, and it is especially dangerous in this respect because, being everywhere touted as nature's 100 per cent health food and the most nearly perfect food, few possess the independence of mind which would enable them to suspect the milk in their diet as responsible for their digestive difficulties. Dr. Kraetzer in an article in *Esquire* of March 1935, "Don't Eat What's Good for You," admits (under pressure, I believe, of general public opinion) that "Milk is a tremendously important food for infants, for some growing children, and for some adults. But," he goes on to say, "because mothers' milk is good for all infants it does not follow that cows' milk—a vastly different fluid—is good for all children and all adults. Milk is a grand food for some people and a very bad one for others. It is certainly not a liquid food, contrary to general belief. When it reaches the stomach it is frequently converted into tough rubbery curds that defy digestion. These decompose when they reach the lower intestine and cause coated tongue, bad breath and a feeling as if the world had gone to ruin. If you are suffering from stomach or intestinal trouble, ask that dispassionate observer, your family doctor, whether milk is good or bad for your particular case." I hold that Dr. Kraetzer's comment, strong as it is, is an understatement of the case against milk. And an overstatement of the insight and independence of milk propaganda, of the average family doctor!

Dr. Eugene Rosamond of Memphis, Tennessee, in an article, "Further Observation on the Evils of Too Much Milk," (*Southern Medical Journal*, Jan. 1935) writes the following:

"The slogan, 'A quart of milk a day for every child,' is good commercial propaganda. It is poor medical advice.

"Nearly 7 per cent of all ailing children who go to the physician are sick because their mothers are forcing them to take more milk than they need. Half again as many 'muddle through' and do not go to the physician. So that at a conservative estimate 10 per cent of the minor ills of childhood are the evils of too much milk.

". . . over enthusiastic mothers, and even physicians have failed to remember that Nature gave a child teeth with which to masticate food stuffs more concentrated [than milk] and of a higher caloric value.

"Trying to fill a 3 or 4-year-old child's stomach with enough milk to meet his caloric needs is like trying to fire a boiler with shavings. The fire box is so full of kindling there is no room for coal. These children are too frequently full and yet not satisfied. They need fuel with more calories before the little engine will run strongly and efficiently. . . .

"Between the ages of 2 and 6 years a quart of milk a day is too much milk. . . .

"The typical symptoms of too much milk are about as follow: the child is pale from anemia, constipated, is cross and irritable and will not eat. Because he will not eat the mother usually insists on still more milk. He is a restless sleeper, grits his teeth, kicks cover and thrashes about, and the majority of them have night terrors. The 'terrors' usually consist of screaming spells, standing up in bed, talking in their sleep, and so on. This in my experience is the most diagnostic of all symptoms. I see night terrors only in milk drinkers. Bed-wetting is, of course, a constant symptom. The child is too full of fluid to do otherwise. Dirt-eating is another not-uncommon occurrence."

Milk is an animal food *for the very young, of the same animal,* and is not a satisfactory food for young animals after the stage of infancy and relative weakness, helplessness, and inability to get about is past; in normal babies in a state of pre-civilization, the development of teeth marks the ending of the period of using milk for food, and begins the era of meat, fish, eggs, and vegetables and fruits, which continues till old age. When in old age the teeth fail, old people may perforce return to the fluid foods of infancy.

Dr. Rabinowitch, Director of the Metabolism Department of the Montreal General Hospital, sees clearly the business-propaganda basis of the vogue for milk as a "health food." "The dairy industries," says he, "would have us flood our tissues with milk. Is milk an indispensable part of the adult's diet? The answer to this question may be found in the natural history of animal and man. Briefly, milk is supplied by the mammalian adult to its young and this supply varies in different species from approximately one month to one year after birth. Thereafter, none of the species in the state of nature is furnished with milk. Milk, therefore, cannot be considered a natural food for the adult animal. From a biological point of view, the mammalian infant may be considered as a parasite on its mother, but in the wisdom of nature, this parasitic habit is discontinued at a comparatively early period in life. In the life history of every species, whether carnivorous or herbivorous—whether its diet consists exclusively of meat or of plants—the transition from the suckling stage to adult life is rapid. The young rabbit changes from a diet of milk to that of leaves in a few days; the young lion from milk to meat; the fruit-eating bat from milk to fruit; and the blood-sucking bat from milk to blood. Since these animals live and continue to propagate, it is obvious that the adult diet must contain all of the necessary food elements which are present in the maternal milk; and man's diet affords no exception to this rule. His geographical distribution is proof of this fact. From prehistoric times to the discovery of America, the milk-produc-

ing animals—the cow, sheep, goat, ass, camel, and reindeer
—were confined to an area approximately from 0° to 70° N.
Latitude and 15° W. to 90° E. Longitude. This includes,
roughly, Europe, Russia and Siberia, India, Persia, Arabia,
and East and North Africa. The rest of the world—Japan,
Australia, China, and Islands in the South Pacific—had no
milk, except for the isolated use of the mare; and yet, within
historical times, the Chinese Empire reached its highest degree of civilization, and to-day, in the interior of China,
where for centuries there has been practically no admixture
of populations, milk is still foreign to the adult diet."

This point of view, which is an unassailable one from any
standpoint (unless we are to accept the necessity of drinking
milk because our food supply as a whole is so bad that it
needs certain mystic substances contained in milk to make it
endurable at all) seems to be one which has never entered the
heads of such experts as Sherman, McCollum, Rose, Barnett
Sure, and the others who speak for scientific nutrition.
These experts talk continually of the importance of milk as
a source of calcium, but they do not make clear why the
adult animal needs any so large supply of calcium or why
the young growing animal, after babyhood, doesn't get sufficient calcium from its other food materials, many of which
contain useful amounts of that mineral—and would contain
far more if it had not been for the misleading propaganda
of the bakers and millers buttressed by the scientific emi-
nence of McCollum, Hertwig, Mendel, and others in favor of
white flour products. Bread and other foods made of
bleached, chemicalized white flour, are for most people the
chief medium for the extraction of essential minerals from
the regular diet; and out of the toleration of this degradation of the commonest foodstuff, has come the *necessity* for

developing and popularizing the new vogue for the "protective foods," milk and green leafy vegetables. After the body
is grown, it would seem that the major need of the tissues for
calcium would be for the repair of the teeth, which surely
require no such amounts as would be represented in the
consumption of a quart of milk each day (unless, as already
noted, the American food supply in general is far worse than
our nutritional mentors have ever dared to admit). But more
important than this is the fact that the calcium taken in
with the food must be assimilable. If the source of calcium
is one that is not well digested because it does not suit the
particular animal at its particular stage of development,
it would do no good if its stomach and intestines were soaked
in solutions of calcium salts.

Articles such as that by Dr. T. Wingate Todd in the
Journal of Home Economics of December 1934, fancifully
and misleadingly titled "An X-Ray Study of Nutritional
Deviations," are written as though the successful living of
the human race apart from dairy herds were an impossible
phenomenon, and one wholly unknown to anthropologists.
This paper, read before the Department of Supervisors and
Teachers of Home Economics of the National Education
Association in Cleveland in February 1934, could hardly
have been differently worded had it been prepared by Dr.
Tobey, well-known paid magnifier of the health values of
milk, or some other employe of the Borden company.
Everything about milk is considered and exploited except
the question of why one needs it after infancy. If "Milk,"
as Dr. Todd (whose qualifications for pronouncements in
this field are apparently a training and skill in surgery)
has said, "is the real source of the master mineral, calcium,
necessary for building bones, maintaining adequate coagula-

bility of the blood, proper muscular tone and vigor, and efficiency of the nervous system," it seems strange to one not intellectually soaked in milk propaganda, that whole races can live and thrive and acquire great strength and endurance without ever touching a drop of milk, or without using any other products of dairy animals.

Every consumer who is being forced into increased use of milk for himself and his family should confront his medical and home-economic informants and advisers, if such there be, with these questions: Why all this pother about milk? Why must I have so much calcium if healthy races find an adequate calcium intake in other common foods? What has happened to the American food supply that makes milk so indispensable just now, and where were the nutrition experts and their writings when this awful degeneration of the dietary that makes the characteristic food of infants so inexplicably necessary to adults, was taking place?

In point of fact calcium is not yet a deficiency in the American dietary of the classes that follow their instincts to a degree, and eschew the characteristic recommendations of home-economic and nutrition teaching, and who can *afford* a decent choice of foods; for adults of smaller income, milk is not an *economical* source of calcium. Borden's and National Dairy Products with their huge salaries to executives, and their chains of subsidiary and interlocked corporations have seen to this latter point. Certainly for many, if not a majority of adults, milk is not fully or satisfactorily digestible in the amounts recommended by milk magnates and their all too bosom friends, the public health officials and university professors.

The Commissioner of Agriculture and Markets of the State of New York even cites in one of his blurbs for New

York's dairy industry, the alkaline reaction produced by milk in the body, as a reason why milk wards off disease. This is now recognized to be unscientific nutritional quackery. As is shown elsewhere in this book, it is impossible for a non-milk drinker or any one else to *avoid* an alkaline reaction in the body except under conditions of starvation or the action of certain poisons.

This great "protective food" is really needed to protect the investments and dividends of Borden's and the other great distributors and the salaries of some teachers and publicity men, far more than it provides any needed and reliable protection to the health of the population beyond infancy and young childhood.

Medical men are much more intelligent on questions of dietary necessity and digestibility than nutrition workers, who have a way of acting as though people could be fitted into the convenient statistical patterns which so well apply to guinea pigs and rats, when a sufficient number are employed in the experiment (and when the responses of those that don't fit the desired conclusions are disregarded). "Milk ALONE," says the American Medical Association in its Exhibit on Nutrition, "is a bulky, often indigestible, constipating, and anemia-producing diet. Patients should not be left on it for long. *Many persons are highly sensitized to milk and should not be forced to take it.*" [Italics mine.]

An article in the journal of the Alabama Medical Association refers to milk as "one of the foods most slowly to be passed out of the stomach. Since milk delays stomach emptying and interferes with the hunger mechanism which one is anxious to stimulate, the advantage of pouring milk into unwilling eaters should be questioned. . . . The midmorning glass of milk so often given is a bad thing for a child with a poor appetite."

". . . In a list of foods drawn up by [Dr.] ALVAREZ [of the Mayo Clinic; May issue of *Modern Medicine*, page 16] showing the greatest offenders by way of indigestion and gastro-intestinal distress, cabbages, apples, tomatoes, milk, and chocolate led all the rest! Milk, in fact, caused severe poisoning more often than anything else among the 100 consecutive patients from whom ALVAREZ drew his list."

The Journal of the American Medical Association in an article by Jay I. Durand, M.D., of Seattle, says: "There is a growing tendency to reduce the amount of milk in infant feeding. Moll believes there is a milk injury due to excessive amounts and characterized by *paleness and an enlarged liver and spleen*. Alfred Hess has stated that *children develop more rickets on a quart than on a pint of milk daily*. The German school sets the limit of 0.5 liter [about one pint] as the total for any one day. While I share the prevalent dislike for rigid laws, in my feeding practice during the past two years I have rarely exceeded this amount. I am convinced that the result has been beneficial and that the method presents no difficulties. It, at least, *necessitates earlier addition of other foods*, encouraging greater variety." [Italics mine.]

An editorial in *The New England Journal of Medicine* for September 13, 1934, speaks almost as plainly as Dr. Rabinowitch, quoted earlier in this chapter, on the question of the fad for the use of milk by adults, and children beyond infancy.

"Examples of fashion in medicine may be found in the

fields of dietetics, of obstetrics, of pediatrics, and of surgery. One of the prevalent dogmata in the feeding of children is that every child must drink a quart of milk and eight ounces of orange juice daily in order that his teeth may grow hard and strong. Whatever the laboratory evidence on which this theory is based, it is probably true that heredity plays a larger part than diet in the characteristics of the teeth, as of the other tissues of the body. In a family of children all fed alike, where one parent has good teeth and the other poor, the qualities of the children's teeth will follow Mendel's law, irrespective of diet. Now milk is not a natural beverage of the human being, or of any other mammal, after the period of infancy. It may be that the human race has become, in a sense, parasitic on the cow; but this parasitism, due to inability or unwillingness of the human female to fulfill her function, need not extend beyond the first year of life. Some children, after drinking the milk and orange juice which are their required quota for breakfast, have little appetite or room left for the bacon, bread, cereal, egg, and fruit which should be the chief staples of their meal.

". . . A little whiskey may be good for one occasionally, but it is not a desirable or exclusive essential of every meal. Other fruits contain vitamin besides oranges."

It would be possible to spend a great deal of space discussing the unsatisfactory condition of the milk supply in respect to its sanitary quality, but that has been briefly discussed in *100,000,000 Guinea Pigs* where among other points it was shown that, according to the annual report of the Massachusetts Department of Health for 1930, nearly a million persons in Massachusetts (i.e., one-fifth of the population) were daily exposed to milk from potentially tuberculous cattle.

At Flemington, New Jersey, in a fine dairy region, there have recently been two serious outbreaks of septic sore throat, one involving 131 cases with two deaths, another involving eighteen cases. The Flemington incident is of course not exceptional with respect to the milk problem either in New Jersey or in any other state. Consumers' Research has in its files many instances of bacterial poisoning of a serious nature from the milk supply. The general state of the art of milk production and distribution is well exemplified by recent information from the State of Indiana, whose Public Health Department's *Monthly Bulletin* reporting for one month, showed 58 of 322 samples or 18 percent illegal on the basis of chemical analysis, while of 320 samples examined bacteriologically 129 specimens, or over 40 percent, were illegal. The condition in other states will likely on the whole be worse, and often very much worse, because Indiana is one which has a well and competently administered public health service that might be regarded as almost perfect in comparison with that of many western and southern states, especially, where the health officer's and food control official's job is often a sinecure and his staff notable for its absence or general inactivity or laziness. (Public documents attest this situation!)

It is significant and natural that the claims made for milk should tend to be based upon the superior product of cows fed upon ideal pasturage. Who indeed does not recall the "contented cows" of the Carnation milk advertising? Cows, however "contented" they may be, do not give first class milk when they are stall fed, as is the preferred practice in

commercial dairy management because of the larger production of milk which is achieved in this way and the simplifica-
tion of the labor, supervision, and other problems of the
dairy, and the reduction of costs of operation. In experiments on animals, testing the vitamin C values of milk, it
was found, for example, that summer milk gave more than
three times the protection against scurvy than was given
by winter milk. The tests have probably not been made—
and if they have been made have not been published—which
would show how serious is the variation in vitamin values
essential to the young child, that take place as a result of
errors in feeding of the cows and commercial practices which
have grown up in order to lessen the cost of milk production.
Nevertheless from what little is known it may be safely
assumed that milk as a "factory product," produced by
cows whose feeding is supervised by agricultural college
teachers and chemists—as the cows of large milk producing
interests tend more and more to be—is a very different and
nutritionally much less desirable substance than milk produced naturally from cows living naturally in fertile pastures. Animals bred specially for milk production and fed
in the manner to give the largest number of quarts of legal
milk per dollar of expenditure in investment and operation
of the dairy farm plant, are something new in the world and
something that, as a source of food supply, the race has
not yet had time to test. This author ventures to predict
that when the test has been completed, we shall find it advantageous to go back to milk produced from cows that are
not bred and cared for as though they were ambulant milk
factories. The present trend in agricultural colleges is
toward experimentation which considers all possibilities for
increasing milk production. Cows are even discouraged from

going after a drink, and the fodder and methods of housing the animals are specially adapted toward achieving maximum production, above all other considerations.

A suspicion is developing in connection with the possible over-use of milk, and such suspicions tend to come along pretty late in the propagation period of a fad, unfortunately for those who "follow the leader" in medical and dietary questions. It is more than possible that an excessive calcium intake may be actually harmful to health, apart from the problem of indigestibility or crowding out of other foods, which itself is a real difficulty and danger to health with many milk drinkers. There is a possibility that undue or excessive use of milk may cause an increased likelihood of the occurrence of the very unpleasant and exceedingly distressing disease of bladder stones (urinary calculi). A recent paper on bladder stone said: "The manifestation of this metabolic disturbance also is revealed by an increase of both calcium and phosphorus in the urine. Polyuria and polydipsia are noted in nearly all cases and are attributed to the increased excretion of calcium and phosphorus. A similar observation was made by McCarrison in his feeding experiments on rats. This increase of calcium and phosphorus in the urine may lead to the formation of urinary calculi."

Another recent finding which is in too early a stage of development to furnish a definitive conclusion but which may be a clue of the greatest importance to a serious dietary menace, is the discovery that cataracts can be produced "in rats within two weeks by feeding them a little more than a third of their ration as galactose. This is a sugar not found as such in nature but formed in the body from milk sugar. As a result of her studies, Dr. Mitchell [of Massa-

chusetts State College and Battle Creek College, Michigan]
believes that some cataracts in humans, particularly those
occurring in diabetes, are due to faulty handling of sugar
by the body [probably milk sugar is meant particularly].
The cataracts produced in her rats were the same kind as
occur in diabetes and in old people." It seems that this experiment might point to the view that when children grow
up or when babies grow into childhood, the characteristic
of their digestion which enables their bodies to take proper
care of some of the substances in milk may change, such
that one or more of the substances in milk become poisons or
organ-overloading or disease-producing elements. It is a
commonplace, of course, that the characteristics of the
digestive tract change as the infant grows into childhood
and adulthood. Even the nature of the bacterial organisms
present in the baby's intestines changes definitely, twice during his development. It is more than likely that there is a
corresponding change in a baby's *capacity to digest milk*,
and that in our body's evolutionary development no provision was made for the digestion of milk beyond that age
at which milk was a natural article of diet regularly provided—by its mother. Certain it is that countless millions
of women lived and raised their young without benefit of
cows during the million years or so in which man's digestive
apparatus was being evolved into its present form, a form
which certainly long antedates the domestication of cows
and goats.

The indigestibility of milk, from which many persons
suffer for years before they clearly isolate the cause extends
so far at times that even the amount of milk or cream drunk
in a cup of coffee or cocoa will cause serious distress. Many
adults, even those who believe in milk as Borden's publicly

do in their advertising, would perhaps find it greatly to their advantage to give up milk entirely for a time, as an experiment to test their own dependence upon it, and to see how its absence may affect their sense of well-being, and perhaps rid them of that slight lumpiness in the region of the digestion which many milk drinkers chronically suffer from. Such a trial period of abstention from milk would of course apply likewise to avoidance of its use in beverages and in ice cream. Home-economists try in every way to increase the amount of milk in the diet, even by use of devices for introducing it into foods where it would not ordinarily appear, just as restaurants and bakeries try by every device possible to increase the amount of sugar consumed in their foods, though sugar is already enormously over-consumed. Both these insidious disadvantages to health (of many persons at least) in the last analysis reflect the end result of a complex and indirect and hardly perceived system of economic drives originating in the need to increase business profits; they are not to be distinguished in any important sense from the radio manufacturers' desire to see a radio set in every room and in every store and shop, and General Motors' wish to sell a second car to every family.

Consumers' Research in one of its bulletins has reported on the very unsatisfactory situation in respect to sanitation in dairying and bottling industries and has shown that grades A and B are often without significance, except that the consumer pays three cents more for a bottle with a special kind of hood over the cap and receives milk neither better than nor indeed different from that which he would have received by purchasing the grade B milk with the plain cap. To people who have paid an extra 3 cents for each of several bottles of milk a day over a period of ten or twenty years, it comes perhaps as a shocking idea to learn that the two "grades" of milk often came out of the same tank or that when they did not, the grade B product may sometimes or often have been equal to or better in actual quality than grade A. Grade A milk could be consistently better than grade B and consistently worth a little more, say half a cent more, but certainly not 3 cents a quart more under any circumstances. If the milk industry were run as it should be, as a necessary public utility safeguarding the health of babies, grade A milk would be the only kind available, and its cost to the consumer would be far less than grade A costs under the present system where the president of a large dairy system gets a salary right up in the top brackets of big incomes, running to a sum more than the total salaries of the President of the United States and half a dozen members of his cabinet.

An adequate discussion of the problem of ice cream, which is the form in which we consume a great deal of our milk and which is everywhere favored as a "health food," even by school teachers, who easily come to confuse an oversweetened dessert with an essential foodstuff, is not possible in the space of this book and must await a more extended treatment of the more important individual items of food supply in a later book. With respect to ice cream, the following correctly represents the situation as well as can be done in the brief space available. Practically every statement made herein is based either upon tests by Consumers' Research or upon assertions clearly made in trade journals of the ice cream industry.

Commercial ice cream, uncontrolled by food laws, is made with dried skim milk, dried egg white, artificial flavor, artificial color, corn sugar, and, indeed, almost anything but honest milk and cream, fruit and fruit flavor, eggs, and other true foodstuffs. Furthermore, modern ice cream nearly always contains a gelatine or gum thickener (which favors germ growth in a mixture that is already a dangerous culture medium for bacteria). This gelatine or gum adulterant facilitates the beating into the mixture of a great quantity of air so as to double its volume; indeed the formulas used in making ice cream are largely determined by the problem of getting the resulting product to hold as much air as possible, as long as possible after serving, and not by any intent to make a product which is good to taste, thoroughly wholesome, and free from harmful bacteria. The consumer pays the same amount for the product as though it were not half air; he eats air, germs, water, and gelatine, instead of the milk and cream he is counting on; and the farmer sells (at an unfavorable price, as "surplus" milk) far less milk than he might have sold if a shrewd and sharp big business corporation and the commercial ice-cream experts of the agricultural colleges had not gotten between him and his market.

"Cherry" ice cream is either made with artificial flavor and no fruit, or with the grossly insanitary, adulterated, and synthetically flavored maraschino cherries which are not at all safe for food for young or old. Ice cream is often a month old before it is sold and may stand around up to 9 months; the most popular flavor (vanilla) moves faster. Ice cream allowed to melt and afterwards refrozen is particularly unsafe. The off-flavored chocolate ice cream is made by mixing the melted returns of all flavors, adding chocolate, and refreezing.

Public health regulations have for the most part lagged far behind in regard to ice cream, which should be as carefully controlled as milk, by medical examination of employes, rigorous specifications and supervision as to raw materials, pasteurization, bacterial standards, design and cleaning of machinery and equipment, and by the licensing of manufacturers.

Early in 1933 a study was made by Consumers' Research on 20 samples of ice cream purchased at various drug stores, candy and stationery shops and cafeterias in New York City, in a middle-class neighborhood swarming with children. Though ice cream should not contain more than 50,000 to 100,000 bacteria per gram, 35 per cent of the samples tested contained more than 100,000. The worst two showed 1,000,000 and 7,500,000 germs per gram. Besides, 35 per cent of the samples contained concentrations of colon bacteria (an indication of most dangerous, disease-breeding contamination by filth) that were from 2 to 10 times higher than the New Jersey Department of Health considers safe for the water of bathing beaches. The well-to-do had no guaranty of safety either for themselves or their children, for several of the highest priced samples showed the worst bacterial contamination. Three of the samples, two cheap and one rather high priced, were fit only to be classed as dilute sewage, and, if New Yorkers had a functioning health department, *would* have been so classed, and their makers and vendors penalized.

One of the County Consumers' Councils—the only one, so far as known to this writer, that carried on any substantial technical, that is, real, activities during that short-lived experiment of the University of Chicago New Dealer, Prof. Paul Douglas—conducted bacteria-count tests on ice cream sold in a small Midwestern city. Not one sample met the government's 50,000-bacteria-per-cubic-centimeter limit, and

XIV

SOME VERY NEW MEANS TO POISON
US ALL—THE FRUIT AND VEGE-
TABLE EXPERTS PREFER AR-
SENIC TO WORM-HOLES

To discuss adequately the thousands of hazards which
beset all who eat commercially produced and packaged and
ready prepared foods, on account of the thousands of kinds
and sources of metallic contaminations that get into our
food supply, is in itself a task that cannot be encompassed
short of a large volume on the subject. Even to prepare an
adequate digest of the great mass of material available on
this subject, much of which has now been assembled for study
and abstracting in the extensive files at Consumers' Research, would be a monumental task requiring full time work
of an able researcher and clerical staff for six months or
more.

The dangers and the number of actual cases of serious
poisoning, followed in some cases by death of the patient,
that were outlined in *100,000,000 Guinea Pigs*, were, according to our present information, considerably understated.
The number of items of our food supply, and that of domestic animals, into which lead, arsenic, copper, selenium,
manganese, and other poisonous metals are now known to
enter in practical and clearly dangerous amounts is so great
that it is impossible for city people even of large income
to avoid the hazard in any way or by any amount of trouble.

For country people who raise a good part of their own food and who buy the rest from neighboring farmers whose methods of husbandry can be noted and watched, a limited measure of protection is possible. One point, however, is exceedingly clear: no one can safely be guided on these matters in this year in this country by the offhand opinions of any chemist or of one's family physician. The technical and scientific literature is indeed so large that properly to read and understand it as it is published would take more time than any physician in private practice could spare from his routine duties. Worse still, the American Medical Association, which is almost the only source of scientific information for the average family practitioner, has consistently devoted very little space to consideration of the question and that which they have given has been for the most part distinguished by its slight, inconspicuous and cautious nature. Chemists, as will elsewhere appear in this book, are interested primarily in means for adulterating and cheapening the food supply (as is especially noteworthy in the case of flour bleaches and bread "improvers," and bakers' supplies of all sorts—see Chapter X), and for them to admit that their public was being *poisoned* by the most triumphant and startling of their discoveries, is a bit too much to ask of human nature. The best way to silence the glib assurances of the chemists on these matters is to remind them of the numerous unexpected poisonings of the radium watch-dial painters in the United States Radium Company's plant, from the results of which 23 factory workers and a chemist died terrible and lingering deaths; of the terrible poisonings which occurred at the time when ethyl (leaded) gasoline was first manufactured, in a plant that was closely supervised by technical experts; of the eminent German chemist, Prof.

Alfred Stock of Berlin, who poisoned both brain and body
by his careless assumption, common to nearly all chemists,
that metallic mercury was a convenient laboratory tool and
not a deadly and insidious poison; of the well-known research
chemist, Dr. Gebauer-Fulnegg of Gary, Indiana, who recently died from an inhalation of the fumes of hydrochloric
acid, one of the commonest and supposedly most harmless of
reagents. On the whole, if you want to know how little
chemists know about poisons, ask any toxicologist, whose
specialty is the effects of poisons on human beings, or ask
the chemist himself what courses he had in toxicology, in his
college work.

The major hazard in connection with arsenic and lead
poisoning from the food supply is, of course, the residues or
coatings that are left on fruits and vegetables which are
now sprayed, almost universally, to protect against the
depredations of insects and fungi. So important is this question from the standpoint of the producer, that *two* bureaus
in the U. S. Department of Agriculture, and one in nearly
every state Department of Agriculture or its equivalent,
exist to help the farmers use more and more potent poisons
against the various moths, worms, and blights which attack
fruits and vegetables, and even ornamental shrubbery and
grasses. The problem has greatly increased in magnitude in
recent years because our extensive and growing practice of
transporting foodstuffs from nearly every part of the country to every other part, in order to be able to defy the
scarcities and imperfections that go with the seasons, carries
almost all the insects and fungi into much wider areas than
they could possibly have reached under any more natural
and less commercial culture. The New York or Virginia
farmer who used to be troubled by imperfections in his fruit

now feels that in order to produce respectable fruit for the market, he must spray almost as hard and as often as the California or Washington grower habitually does. The grower who sprays most and most often, necessarily sets the pace for the others. If consumers can find apples with no imperfections, they will on the whole not purchase apples with a few worm holes or scald marks. If cabbage grows bigger and less of the crop is lost, with heavy doses of arsenate of lead, all the cabbage growers come in due time to be big customers of the insecticide firms, whose stock in trade is poisons of diverse and deadly sorts.

The numerous poisonings that occur are not played up in the press. When on account of the number involved, a story does force its way into the newspapers, the sale of the vegetable or fruit involved falls off alarmingly—as in one city where the sale of a certain kind of cabbage dropped 50 per cent overnight due to alarm at seizures occasioned by the reckless use of lead arsenate by growers. Farm animals are frequently poisoned by browsing under the orchard trees, or licking their branches; farm laborers are commonly affected, though the harm done will not appear until some years have elapsed, as a rule, and then may not be associated with the real cause but attributed to some other factor. The meat and milk from affected farm animals is of course poisoned, and the liver, where the metallic poisons are filtered out of the blood stream and stored for later elimination, though especially valued as a food for persons with certain dangerous illnesses, may in some cases actually contain sufficient poison to be apparent to the eye.

While nutrition experts are debating whether copper is a normal element (in minute quantities) in the human body and in the natural diet, the *Journal of the American Medi-*

cal Association, on July 15, 1933, remarked: "Obviously, people consume quite unwittingly, day by day, far larger quantities of copper than the data presented indicate. Probably there is more actual danger at present of excessive intake than of deficiency in the human dietary. . . . Intensive study of the problem for man is imperative."

This is but one of the many absurd failures of nutrition workers to learn something of the work of entomologists and toxicologists; their failure to study these poisons has been a very dangerous error of omission for that portion of the population which in one way or another derives its ideas of good diet from the nutrition scientists, via home-economics teachers and social workers, for example.

In order to reduce the problem to the reasonable dimensions essential to the scope of the present brief work, I shall in formulating a useful summary of some of the major hazards confine the study mainly to the medical and scientific publications of one group of researchers in the field: Dr. C. N. Myers, Dr. Binford Throne, Dr. Laird Van Dyck, Dr. John A. Fordyce, Dr. Isadore Rosen, Dr. Leon H. Cornall, Dr. E. F. Mueller, Dr. G. P. Metz, Miss Eleanor Marples, Miss Florence Gustafson, and Mr. Jerome Kingsbury. Their findings are given in a group of papers presented before scientific and medical societies. Anyone who doubts the validity of their views and findings as abstracted herein should refer to some of the original papers easily obtainable through any large library, since only a hasty survey of some of their contents can be given in this brief digest.

Dr. C. N. Myers, speaking of copper poisoning (and this is by far the least threatening of the types of metal poison-

ing that now beset us), says: "Copper has a widespread use
as an algaecide [to kill algae, small plant forms in city
water, reservoirs, swimming pools, and the like], is used
extensively in various kinds of utensils, particularly as a
competitor for aluminum, resulting in a great deal of unscientific propaganda for and against either metal. The use
of copper as an insecticide [copper acetoarsenite], on fruit
and vegetables, dates back many years and enough has been
spread on the soil to make it an element readily found.
Lythgoe (1926) examined 1,544 samples of liquor and 163
of them contained copper. . . . It is a well-known fact that
copper is a common constituent present in shell fish and
certain types of crustaceans. These, however, should be expected inasmuch as large quantities of copper solutions of
one kind or another are poured into the waters in which
these fish live. . . . During the past few years examination of
various foods has been carried out and very generally copper
is found as a contaminating substance varying from 2 mg.
to 100 mg. per kilo [2 to 100 parts per million] of food.
One of the most interesting developments noted recently was
the work of Hart (1929) in which the dried egg yolk was
analyzed and it was found that there was present 0.00076
percent copper [7.6 parts per million], the white showing
0.00056 percent copper [5.6 parts per million]. . . . Mallory observed ten cases of hemochromatosis [a discoloration
of skin and tissues by deposition of pigment from the blood,
caused by copper] . . . at the Boston City Hospital within
the course of a single year. . . . Mallory has also indicated
the presence of copper in apple butter, coffee, tea and water.
He states that the brass water pipes [brass is the commonest
alloy of copper] in Brookline are so eroded that a pin may
be thrust through them at any point. . . . Hess (1924) has

found that milk pasteurized by running over copper pipes
may contain as high as 2 mg. of copper per liter [2 parts
per million] and that this interferes with the action of vitamin C so that scurvy is produced." Copper is far less toxic
than lead; indeed some of what has passed for copper poisoning may have been due to more dangerous substances such
as lead or arsenic present in copper as contaminants, but it
is the present view that its dangers have been greatly under-
estimated in the past.

In Dr. Myers' opinion arsenic is the fulminating or "ex-
plosive" metallic contamination in the body which may un-
derlie sudden appearance of trouble with the skin, nervous
controls, or the eyes. From earliest times, arsenic has been
used to kill enemies or to cure disease, and since the early
18th century it has been a common ingedient of a tonic
medicine prescribed by physicians. Many other medicines,
including rhubarb-and-soda, calamine lotion, glucose, and
sulphur ointment may often include an arsenical contamination. As early as 1900, experts in America and abroad were
noting the carelessness of Americans in the use of arsenic in
industry and agriculture and other fields. In 1927 experiments were reported on the very effective killing of mosquito
(anopheline) larvae, *near an oyster shucking plant*. In three
hours, 98 per cent of the larvae were dead—and quite likely
some very large percentage of the oysters became arsenic
carriers—to whom it might concern! Dr. Myers well says:
"It is difficult to state which is more distressing, malaria or
arsenic eczema, a large crop of cotton or a systemic disturbance in the human, large perfect leaves of tobacco or smaller
insect-eaten leaves without disease." He sums up the high
arsenic content of sea foods; crabs showed 36 to 70 p.p.m.
(parts per million) of arsenic and scallops 36 to 85 p.p.m.

Arsenic in the urine rose, after the consumption of lobster by a human subject, to 136 times its normal value for 36 hours after the lobster meal. Try to find that study reported in the work of home-economics experts or of the state and federal bureaus of fisheries! Skin patients who are having trouble eliminating arsenic, are at once forbidden fish.

In 1922 the Home and Colonial Stores sold cocoa containing the large amount of 3.6 p.p.m. of arsenic, and Rowntree's brand contained 14.3 p.p.m. (a very large proportion) derived from the potassium carbonate used to render cocoa soluble. Of 9 samples of leading brands of cocoas analyzed for Consumers' Research in 1934, 4 samples contained no arsenic, but the other 5 contained from 3 to 36 p.p.m. making the average arsenic content 9.8 p.p.m. (No brand was found uniformly free from arsenic.) The presence of an amount of arsenic greater than 1.43 p.p.m. (0.01 grains of As_2O_3 per pound) is nominally prohibited under the regulations of the Federal Food and Drug Administration and by most state food and drug control departments; even this "official tolerance" is far above a safe amount. Therefore, even by the government's own standards adopted thirty-one years ago—long before such work as that of Myers, Throne and others cited in this book had even been begun—the average of 9.8 p.p.m. of arsenic in cocoas represents a pronounced hazard to consumers. Baking powder shows amounts up to 7 p.p.m., and self-rising flour also commonly has arsenic contaminations. Children especially should be guarded against eating any large quantities of chocolate, chocolate candies or chocolate products. The obscurity of the causes of such poisoning is well illustrated by the sack of sugar which absorbed an arsenical liquid oozing out of a leaky can shipped in the same railway car. In another case, sea water ran off hides that had been dehaired with an arsenic salt, onto meat stored below decks, and left large amounts of the arsenic on the meat. Liquid weed killer used on farms to control noxious weeds has killed men and cattle and poisoned much milk and meat besides. Sheep are dipped into arsenical baths. A market gardener died after 8 years of slow poisoning from the use of poisons in his fields. Arsenic has appeared as a pigment in wall papers, and bread and candy wrappers. Cigarettes contain large amounts of both arsenic and lead, above even the generous limits set by the Food and Drug Administration for foods and beverages; yet the inhalation of smoke into the lungs presents a more dangerous means for the absorption of arsenic and lead than does the ingestion of poisoned foods into the stomach. This is because the lungs have no organ corresponding to the liver, which could protect the body from poisonous fumes or smoke.

The view of Myers and his co-workers is that the government's generous limit of 1/100 grain per pound or gallon of food or beverage is absurd, and they imply in their cautious way that its enforcement is in effect nil, or nearly so, as their own findings on the amount of arsenic present on apples, cherries, peaches, and so on, tend to show quite clearly. Even cotton cloth (used, of course, in brewing of coffee in restaurants!) contains arsenic. The gases given off by storage batteries have contained arsenic in large quantities.

Printing ink contains so much arsenic that news dealers have been affected. Glycerine found in many drug products commonly contains much arsenic. "Gelatin and glucose," says Myers, "are the most common articles that should always be held under suspicion. Gelatin is used extensively as a filler in a variety of desserts and yet it is a common source of contamination, amounts being found up to 10 parts per million. Glucose [corn starch, syrup, usually called corn syrup] is a substance extensively used in baby foods, delicatessen products, in syrups used in preparing canned fruits, and in syrups at the soda water fountain. One need only observe the growth of the sales of soda fountain and delicatessen products to realize the widespread possibility of contamination."

In another place Myers and Throne have said: "The annual per capita consumption of sugar in 1823 was 9 pounds, equivalent to 44 calories per day, and in 1924 more than 110 pounds represents the corresponding value with an average daily consumption of 547 calories. Little thought is necessary to observe that our daily habits have materially changed in a century and that we are suffering from a malady of 'carbohydratism.' This enormous consumption of carbohydrate is a national dietary fault due to overindulgence in sugars. In 1926 a Department of Commerce Survey of 80 per cent of the candy makers of the nation produced 1,083,399,754 pounds. This is equivalent to 9 pounds for every man, woman, and infant."

In a table of arsenic contents of common foods, Myers lists determinations which show the very high amounts for fish, *sulphur-treated* dried fruits, cabbage, lettuce, corn, dried peas, and low amounts for carrots, beef, veal. He mentions the tendency among farmers to feed cattle (and horses) with arsenic to improve the appearance of their coats, and remarks on the end result of such treatment—which the shrewd purchaser always guards against, by not buying stock that have been sleeked with tonic doses of arsenic. The need for protection by the farmer of the consumer of meat and milk from such animals (the horse meat even, goes into dog food!) is, of course, not discussed. Farmers under a profit system must protect *themselves* as consumers, but cannot afford to take effective steps to protect the consumers of their products.

Throne and Myers have reported that 30 per cent of all cases coming into their skin clinic diagnosed as eczema are sufferers from a complication of arsenic poisoning and the condition usually described as eczema. Examination of blood and urine of patients having scleroderma (a chronic disease of the skin in which it becomes hardened and thickened, sometimes resulting in death) and certain types of psoriasis shows dangerous amounts of arsenic. Arsenic poisoning and jaundice often occur together, and when they do, often cause death, on account of the grave liver impairment which arsenic causes.

Arsenical skin cancers are known to have followed medication with arsenical tonics taken by mouth, after an interval of many years. This effect of arsenic received into the body in large amounts by workmen and miners has been known for centuries, but the dangerous medical doctrine that small amounts of almost any poison can be taken for either a long or short period, is completely refuted by the large number of cases of malignant disease of the skin following, often years later, upon use of arsenic in agricultural spraying operations, or as a "medicine."

The writer of this book would consider with grave doubt the competence of a physician who, in the face of these findings, would administer arsenic in a tonic in any form or any amount. Further, he would not take any tonic prescribed by a physician or offered as a patent medicine without being absolutely certain of the name of every ingredient. Many physicians' prescriptions, and a great number of patent medicines, contain arsenic because of its traditional "tonic" and temporary complexion-improving properties. It will be a generation at least before physicians generally give up the use of such treatments, just as custom has kept them using the common drug store solution of *Mercurochrome* for years after findings very unfavorable to its antiseptic qualities were given wide circulation among the practitioners who have time and professional interest enough to read professional journals.

Arsenic, as well as lead and fluorine, attack us from a number of directions, many quite unexpected. Says Myers: "Arsenic gains entrance to our bodies through unexpected sources and as previously pointed out by me, apples containing four times the medicinal dose have been examined. Arsenic is found on peaches, pears, cherries, lettuce, tomatoes, celery, in our shell fish and sea foods and even in the cotton goods which we may wear. These are all highly contaminated with arsenic, thus making more difficult the existence of the unfortunate susceptible individual.

"It should not be overlooked that life in its essential characteristics is being carried on under artificial conditions."

Myers notes: "Furthermore, it may not be realized that the insecticide industry has increased in leaps and bounds, thus increasing the opportunities for exposure. [The amount of lead and arsenic now used in this form runs to approximately ½ pound per person per year, and a millionth of that amount of arsenic, and a far *less* quantity of lead, is more than should be permitted on a pound of any food!] The average individual little realizes that the grapes used for beverages may be highly contaminated with arsenic which has been sprayed upon the fruit during its growing season. In order to make the insecticide adhere more firmly such substances as casein have been employed. During the dry season little opportunity for removal of this spray residue is possible [by the rain] and during the pressing of the fruit for juice the arsenic may be carried mechanically into the product. . . . It is my belief that concern should be directed more particularly toward subchronic arsenic poisoning in which the absorption of relatively small amounts of arsenic over a long period of time will produce conditions which simulate many other diseases. The late phases of arsenic disturbances of a subchronic nature are such manifestations as local disturbances of sensation and motion, particularly the hands and feet, characteristic of a beginning peripheral neuritis, intense headaches, associated with no other causative factor, pains in the joints and the extremities, paralysis especially of the extensor muscles of the toes. There are cases available in the literature in which paralysis begins in the extensor muscles of the hands and arms. . . . Paralysis may occur within a few hours or even many months after the beginning of the symptoms. From the treatment point of view it is very important to call attention to the fact that recovery from paralysis is a very slow process and that even arsenic may be excreted for many years following the onset of symptoms. In cases of long duration the patient may become apathetic and dull."

As to lead, Myers points out, as has Consumers' Research in a number of items in its bulletins, that "In the city a constant barrage of lead particles is being poured out by the ever-increasing number of motor vehicles. [The source of such lead is of course in the now almost universal use of the deadly ethyl fluid in gasoline as an anti-knock compound.] . . . The fruit and vegetables consumed by us is an additional source of lead, arsenic and copper, as well as the cotton goods worn by us. It is important at this time to quote from a report by Wright, Sappington and Rantoul:

'In the Industrial Clinic of the Massachusetts General Hospital it was found that almost 11 percent of the cases of lead poisoning studied over a period of many years (1911 to 1923) were of non-industrial origin, for the most part associated with the consumption of lead-piped waters, of home distilled alcohol, or of home-made wines. This group was, in size, second only to that of painters. In addition to the cases seen as hospital patients, many others were found upon local investigation of home conditions, a total number so impressive as to indicate that non-industrial lead poisoning existed in New England as a public health problem of importance. As lead pipes are widely used in other parts of the country it was felt that a similar situation might be encountered elsewhere, particularly in regions supplying soft waters.' "

Cases of serious poisoning from water supply have been reported, from amounts of lead contamination as small as 1/10 milligram per day, an amount so small as to be almost inconceivable to the layman, being approximately one five-millionth of a pound in each day's total drinking water consumption. Considering that there are about 150 trades, including even a number of kinds of *office* work in which the individual is exposed to lead in the air or in contacts with skin, and that hundreds of cases are recorded in medical literature of babies that have been gravely poisoned by lead paints used on floors and porches and articles around the home, it is clear that the danger is a great and increasing one. The most menacing type of poison, of course, is one whose effects are obscure or delayed, since cause and effect are so difficult to relate, in such cases, even for the expert physician. Lead and arsenic, especially the latter, are exactly such poisons, and the author verily believes that the death rate from typical end results of arsenic, lead, and fluorine poisoning—cancer, for example—could rise rapidly or be doubled or trebled within a few years. This would come about because of the conventional and tolerated suppression by the government of information, in the possession of its officers and scientific experts, on menaces to health whose increase or continuance undisturbed has commercial or economic value to some interest. The increase of the hazard and of ill health and loss of life due to it could, in the present corrupt alliance of food and drug administrative officials with commercial agencies producing and otherwise having a commercial interest in the distribution of commercial poisons, go on without public authorities bringing the probable cause of the situation, well known to medical specialists in this field, to the general public attention in any way. A government whose Bureau of Public Health is estopped by official order of a Secretary of the Treasury at the instance of the meat packers, from warning the population against the (supposed) dangers of eating large amounts of meat in summer is not a government which is going to harm the paint trade or the cotton or the wool trade, or the agriculturists' interest in increased consumption of meat, apples, cabbage, celery, and milk, by pointing out the menacing amounts of poisons which these foods regularly contain. The government officials have a very nice alibi in cases of this kind: it would harm the consumer for the government to inform him, they say, of the dangers to which he exposes himself in eating sprayed lettuce or apples or poisoned milk or fish because he cannot afford to be deprived of the benefits to health in these kinds of food. Better, therefore, let him be poisoned than to let him run the risk of deficiency disease because of his being taught to avoid the dangerous foods whenever they are produced or marketed under conditions not assuring their freedom from contamination.

Surely some bright lad from high school can be counted on to stand up and tell the government scientific experts what is wrong with this scholarly, and cowardly, bureaucratic mode of reasoning.

The well-to-do can escape these dangers to some degree, since they are accentuated by ill health, poor and cheap foods, cheap liquor, and chronic constipation. Some of these are evils which comfortably situated people can often avoid, except the last named, perhaps, which will be worse among the white collar people and those who live without working. But in a country where even the bird and wild animal population is being sharply decreased by the poisoning of *their* food supply in orchard and field so that a grasshopper, once a certain and safe article of diet for the robin, may now be an *arsenic*-poisoned grasshopper whose effect on the bird's insides may be disastrous; when even the bees have been killed in huge numbers by poison-sprayed blossoms on fruit trees and the orchard herbage under the trees; there can be no certainty for anyone. It is interesting to note that the commercial beekeeper has, for business reasons, been able to obtain the enactment of laws in certain states for the protection of his property from the dangers of spray residues; on the other hand the consumer has thus far been unable to obtain the passage of laws providing him with protection from the hazards of poisoning from lead and arsenic spray residues. A bee is a commercial asset, whereas up to the present time the slow poisoning of consumers in masses has not been seriously considered by commercial interests— whether beekeepers or food manufacturers—from the standpoint of its effect upon the market for consumers' goods.

The increasing amount of baldness, even, is a symptom of the widespread nature of the danger; 75 per cent of 198 cases of a certain type showed arsenic and lead in pathologic amounts in the urine, and improvement in such cases occurred when a certain treatment to eliminate the metals was followed. In a number of cases that were tested, arsenic was further positively identified *as present in the skin* of the affected area.

In ending one of his papers, Dr. Myers said: "The promiscuous use of insecticides on our fruits and vegetables is a factor that the consuming public should not tolerate. The use of enormous quantities of insecticide is a distinct menace to health. The universal dusting or spraying of cotton fields is a factor that may bring about untoward effects among the general population, affecting not only those who are within the cotton field district, but the dust may be carried in the air and fall on other vegetation or individuals who are susceptible to the condition. The same situation is true in regard to the use of arsenic preparations as larvacides and the pouring of large amounts of toxic material into waters from which fish and crustaceans are to be taken for human consumption. [It is reported that there is often sufficient of toxic insecticidal substances washed into streams from orchards, the soil of which drains into lakes and brooks, that fish are no longer able to maintain life in the poisoned water. Fish taken far out at sea, while they would contain natural arsenic present in ocean waters, would, of course, also be contaminated with arsenic and other metals, but these would be present in probably considerably less toxic compounds.] The promiscuous spraying of the public with small particles of lead from the exhaust of automobiles in time is bound to show its influence on individuals susceptible to lead as a poison.

"It has become a routine procedure in our laboratories to examine the urine of patients for arsenic and lead and it has been extremely surprising to note that so many individuals show pathologic amounts of lead. . . . Laxity in giving consideration to the small amount of metal involved may allow the case to pass by undiagnosed. Every effort has been made to show that extremely minute amounts of metallic compounds may be the cause of marked disturbances in the normal functions. It is further shown that during an intoxication such as jaundice arsenic may be absent or even present in only traces. Metals of all kinds are potentially dangerous even in small amounts and the aim should be to strive for their absence rather than to regulate the amount."

Dr. Throne reported that in 52 per cent of eczema cases in infants and young children, tests of the urine showed dangerous amounts of arsenic. The milk of nursing mothers whose babies suffered from eczema showed arsenic was present in 72 per cent of the cases examined. Moreover, in 15 cases where eczema was not present, 13 showed a total absence of arsenic, and in the remaining two cases the amount of arsenic found was very small.

A case is reported of a child who was sensitive to several kinds of food, and who, upon removal from the body of retained arsenic, was able to eat with impunity those foods that had hitherto caused a reaction of asthma or urticaria.

Dr. Throne, discussing one of Dr. Myers's papers, emphasized "that the most important element in producing chronic metal poisoning is not medication but the constant exposure to small amounts of metals, either through food contamination or through occupational contact."

Dr. A. F. Kraetzer, discussing one of Dr. Myers's papers, mentioned an interesting case which exhibits the extremely insidious and alarming nature of metallic poisoning. A woman "brought several newly painted oil sketches home from the country and put them up around her apartment to dry. Within two days every inmate of the household was sick. The woman herself was violently ill with high fever, erythema multiforme, urticaria, asthma and vasomotor rhinitis. . . . Her husband developed pallor, weakness and a corneal ulcer. Her sister and the cook had severe abdominal cramps. Even the house pets were involved, the dog getting eczema and the cat an enteritis."

Dr. Ernest Ellsworth Smith reported on a noted case of epidemic poisoning in Southern France, the cause of which was not located until nearly 200 years later—in metallic lead which formed a part of cider and wine presses (used on account of its durability and apparent resistance to corrosion and the ease with which it is worked, exactly the reasons which have put lead piping into contact with the water supply systems which serve millions, possibly, of people in the United States—400 years later).

In the field of this book, the most important sources of lead and arsenic, by far, are the residues from insect sprays on fruits and vegetables. On the point, it is important that from 1919 to 1929 the consumption of the salts of poisonous metals in the destruction of insects increased fourfold. The work of the earliest technical investigators in the field, hard-driven by the increasing economic interest and influence of agriculture and the chemical industries, tended to come to such amazing conclusions as that no one was likely to die from a single meal containing insecticide-sprayed fruit or vegetables. Yet even that cold and stupid conclusion has been belied by a number of cases of death from a single accidental dose of poison received in this way. Even within the last few years, experts working with rats, notorious for their ability to consume toxins and unsavory and unwholesome foods, have drawn the wholly unwarranted conclusion that insect poisons were nothing that need to be considered with alarm, and a score or more of chemists and entomologists and some governmental experts and regulatory officials have written to Consumers' Research violently protesting their disbelief in the warnings of Consumers' Research against these hazards, and assuring us that the unscientific nature of our work was clearly shown by our willingness to assume that broccoli or cabbage or pears, known to carry toxic or fatal amounts of lead arsenate, might some day be eaten by someone with fatal results. As to the possibility of slow poisoning over a long period with ultimate cancerous lesions, these men and a home-economist or two have uniformly taken the ground, in effect, that no one was likely to be injured by a poison that he could not see or taste or get an immediate bellyache from. A fine position for chemists and entomologists, indeed, whose elaborate and costly techniques have largely been developed in order to solve problems that were beyond the capacity of people to solve who could determine poisons only by touch or taste or feel, or by a pain in the gut! Some day we shall perhaps assemble some of these letters for publication to lay before students of education the very serious problem of whether or not persons who have been given a false economic or social conditioning can really learn to be anything more than skilled artisans, on the basis of the training afforded by present-day college courses in sciences and the technical arts. One thing we are sure of—that, as in the case of many eminent nutritionists, an instinct for the social welfare and for honest workmanship among scientists is more vital to society than an excessive devotion to the minutiae of differential rat-diets or trace-quantities of silver in smelter-gases.

People who can accept and carry on their daily work by the idea that arsenical poisons are dangerous to the foliage of an apple tree and must be tested and applied with extreme caution and under scientific control to avoid ruining an orchard or a garden; that they are fatal to the insects which consume them in the search for food; and that in spite of these facts these deadly tree and insect poisons cannot harm the human being who eats them in unknown and highly variable amounts upon or in scores or hundreds of different foods and food ingredients, are, as has been indicated elsewhere, people who are only to be trusted in the narrow enterprise of reading galvanometers, measuring out cubic centimeters of liquid, sucking on a pipette,—and like as not, poisoning themselves a bit in the process, as many have done.

The following table, based on data presented by Myers, Throne, Gustafson, and Kingsbury in their paper on "Significance and Danger of Spray Residue," in *Industrial and Engineering Chemistry* of June, 1933, will indicate some of the dangers in the limited field of spray residues. Some of the most alarming indications of this table are the presence of the poisonous metals *inside* the fruits and vegetables tested; with sometimes more in the interior than on the surface, and the extreme variations that are possible, so that

clearly, short of thoroughgoing governmental control, no
measure will possibly suffice to protect either the infant who
to begin with is perhaps nearly free of arsenic in his skin
and lead in his growing bones, or the adult who may have a
good deal of both pretty generally scattered through the
body.

DETERMINATION OF ARSENIC AND LEAD IN FOODS
(September, 1932)

Food Analyzed	No. of Samples	Av. % Solids	Parts of Arsenic per Million of Solids	No. of Samples	Parts of Lead per Million of Solids
Celery tops	3	12.4	0.0 –1.36	2	34.8 – 54.7
Celery, unwashed	3	5.66	0.0 –1.07	2	5.0 – 8.07
Celery, washed	3	5.89	0.0 –3.34	2	26.9 – 40.
Celery heart	1	11.2	0.0	1	73.0
Eggplant skin	3	16.9	0.0	2	15.0 – 39.4
Eggplant pulp	4	7.45	0.0 –2.31	2	35.8 – 41.2
Eggplant pulp and skin	1	4.15	3.84	2	58.1 – 61.5
Iceberg lettuce, washed	3	3.44	0.0 –0.45	2	0.0 – 25.2
Iceberg lettuce heart..	1	6.09	0.0	2	80.4 – 82.8
Boston lettuce, unwashed	3	2.64	0.0	2	15.4 – 17.9
Boston lettuce, washed	3	4.16	0.0 –3.33	1	9.4
Cabbage, unwashed ...	3	6.14	0.0 –3.26	2	29.6 – 36.9
Cabbage, washed	3	5.31	0.0 –2.57	2	38.1 – 49.3
Cabbage heart	1	9.5	0.0	2	30.3 – 53.7
Broccoli stem	1	11.6	0.0	2	11.5 – 12.9
Broccoli leaves	3	20.0	0.1 –2.52	2	0.0
Broccoli	3	16.3	0.0 –0.22	1	27.1
Carrot tops	3	41.6	0.0 –4.10	2	5.1 – 44.9
Carrot skin	3	14.5	0.0 –0.7	2	0.0 – 9.7
Carrot pulp	3	12.3	0.0 –1.04	1	11.7
Carrot and skin, unwashed	3	10.10	Trace	2	0.0 – 9.3
Carrot and skin, washed	1	8.34	0.4	2	1.8 – 12.2
Storage carrot and skin	2	8.38	0.7	2	18.3 – 38.0
Storage carrot pulp ...	1	5.74	0.0	2	0.0 – 0.0
Storage carrot skin ...	1	1.26	0.0	2	0.0 – 3.3
Green pepper skin and pulp	2	4.63	0.0 –1.21	2	0.0 – 94.1
Green pepper skin.....	1	7.7	0.0	1	0.0
Green pepper pulp	1	1.5	Trace	1	25.8
Beet greens	1	6.09	0.0	2	36.2 – 42.1
Beet pulp and skin....	2	17.05	0.0	2	10.8 – 37.0
Beet pulp	2	10.2	Trace	2	89.8 –159.0
Tomato skin	2	16.2	Trace	2	24.0 – 54.9

DETERMINATION OF ARSENIC AND LEAD IN FOODS
—Continued

Food Analyzed	No. of Samples	Av. % Solids	Parts of Arsenic per Million of Solids	No. of Samples	Parts of Lead per Million of Solids
Tomato pulp	3	5.13	0.0 –1.46	2	16.1 – 16.5
Tomato blossom	1	10.5	0.0	1	72.1
String beans, yellow, unwashed	1	8.5	Trace	1	7.0
String beans, yellow, washed	1	7.38	0.3	2	0.0 – 57.4
Pea shells	1	21.39	0.2	2	0.0 – 0.0
Peas	1	60.0	0.0	2	47.7 – 48.3
Lima bean shells	1	24.5	Trace	2	0.0 – 13.1
Lima beans	1	26.6	3.57	2	7.9 – 4.15
String beans, green, unwashed	1	8.68	Trace	2	47.5 – 74.1
String beans, green, washed	1	8.75	0.45	2	5.0 – 5.2
Spinach, unwashed	1	10.9	0.0	2	0.0 – 8.7
Spinach, washed	1	10.9	Trace	2	0.0 – 74.0
California peach skin, unwashed	1	14.2	1.29	2	31.5 – 72.8
California peach skin, washed	1	16.0	0.0	2	49.9 – 61.0
California peach pulp..	1	11.5	0.32	2	4.2 – 18.5
Elberta peach skin, unwashed	1	21.7	0.0	2	134.0 –168.0
Elberta peach skin, washed	1	22.0	0.0	2	123.0 –159.0
Elberta peach pulp....	2	9.1	0.1 –0.3	2	1.9 – 5.2
Apple skin, unwashed..	1	21.2	0.0	2	0.0 – 83.6
Apple skin, washed....	1	32.2	0.0	2	0.0 – 57.0
Apple blossom and stem	1	19.1	20.0	1	539.0
Apple pulp	3	13.3	0.2 –1.25	2	3.8 – 18.0
Apple core	1	16.4	0.83	2	160.0 –199.0
Blue plums, skin, unwashed	1	27.8	Trace	2	0.17– 0.24
Blue plums, skin, washed	1	25.8	Trace	2	0.0 – 45.1
Blue plums, pulp......	2	16.4	0.0	2	1.4 – 16.7
Pears, skin, unwashed.	2	23.8	Trace	2	0.17– 0.24
Pears, skin, washed ...	1	23.8	0.0	2	66.0 – 99.0
Pears, pulp	3	6.8	0.0 –0.3	2	0.9 – 19.6
Pears, blossom	1	55.8	Trace	1	59.5
Pears, core	1	14.9	0.0	2	35.0 – 45.0
Blue grapes, unwashed.	1	13.2	0.21	2	6.2 – 38.8
Blue grapes, washed...	1	13.1	0.0	1	32.7
Green grapes, unwashed	1	10.7	0.0	2	33.0 – 49.0
Green grapes, washed..	1	11.9	0.12	2	29.1 – 29.5

The authors just cited also report the case of a young girl attending a university in Pennsylvania who died after three days' illness following the eating of sprayed apples. A similar case occurred at Northwestern University following the eating of asparagus by a number of young women. "Analysis of the asparagus showed the presence of considerable arsenic, very much in excess of that which would be tolerated by any pure food laws [*J. Am. Med. Assoc.*, 99, 2202 (1932)]. . . . . In one instance individuals suffering with arsenic poisoning reported that their physician had associated their metallic intoxication with the consumption of celery soup made from fresh stalks. In another instance, the consumption of grape juice was involved." And again, "Many months ago broccoli was served at a dinner given by a large group of medical men. Approximately 100 of the individuals present suffered with varying degrees of gastro-intestinal symptoms and several had to be sent to the hospital. Arsenic and lead were found in the broccoli."

Speaking of the high arsenic content of representative samples of fish, Myers and his co-workers remark: "The values found show the relation of the use of insecticide for the purpose of destroying larvae: man destroys the larvae; the fish eat the larvae; and man eats the fish." This brief sentence might well have been captioned by the heading: How grateful we should all be to the science of Entomology!

Not content with contaminating our food supply with copper, arsenic, and lead, entomologists and agricultural scientists are now turning to still more dangerous insecticides—mercury, selenium, manganese, fluorine, and others. "The exceedingly deadly nature of mercuric compounds" causes even the Food and Drug Administration "the gravest apprehension"; and "selenium," says the F. and D. A., "produces effects upon higher animals which can only be characterized as 'ghastly!'" In the past, manganese poisoning has been a rare type of malady threatening only workers in industry, but if the use of manganese compounds as an insecticide increases, it is probable also that consumers will be widely affected. Its results upon the body, too, are ghastly, and no method of alleviating them is known.

BRIEF BIBLIOGRAPHY OF REFERENCES APPLICABLE TO THE FOREGOING CHAPTER

"Significance and Danger of Spray Residue," by C. N. Myers, Binfood Throne, Florence Gustafson, and Jerome Kingsbury. Reprinted from *Industrial and Engineering Chemistry*, June, 1933.

"The Medico-Legal Aspects of Chronic Metallic Poisoning," by C. N. Myers. Reprinted from *International Journal of Medicine and Surgery*, July-December, 1932.

"Arsenic Findings in Eczema and Allied Conditions in Infants and Young Children," by Laird Van Dyck, Binford Throne, and C. N. Myers. Reprinted from *Archives of Pediatrics*, April, 1930.

"Action of Sodium Thiosulfate in Treatment of Metallic Intoxications and Lesions of the Skin," by Eleanor Marples and C. N. Myers. Reprinted from the *Proceedings of the Society for Experimental Biology and Medicine*, 1926.

"Health Hazards from the Ingestion of Small Amounts of Metals," by C. N. Myers and Binford Throne. Reprinted from *New York State Journal of Medicine*, October 15, 1929.

"Arsenic as an Etiological Factor in the Genesis of Eczema," by Binford Throne, Laird Van Dyck, Eleanor Marples, and C. N. Myers. Reprinted from *New York State Journal of Medicine*, October 15, 1926.

"Normal Arsenic and Its Significance from the Point of View of Legal Medicine," by C. N. Myers and Leon H. Cornall. Reprinted from *The American Journal of Syphilis,* October, 1925.

"The Relation of Arsenic to Public Health," by C. N. Myers and Binford Throne. Reprinted from *New York State Journal of Medicine,* July 15, 1929.

"Quantitative Studies in Syphilis from a Clinical and Biologic Point of View, II Normal Arsenic," by John Fordyce, Isadore Rosen, and C. N. Myers. Reprinted from *Am. J. M. Sc.* 164: 242, 1922.

"Arsenic Findings in Dermatological Conditions," by Binford Throne, Laird Van Dyck, Eleanor Marples, and C. N. Myers. Read at the Annual Meeting of the Medical Society of the State of New York, at Niagara Falls, May 10, 1927.

"Treatment of Arsenical Eczema," by Binford Throne, Laird Van Dyck, Eleanor Marples, and C. N. Myers. Reprinted from *New York State Journal of Medicine,* December 1, 1926.

"Arsenic as a Problem in Present Day Public Health Management," by C. N. Myers, Laird Van Dyck, and Binford Throne; Reprinted from *The Medical Times,* New York, May, 1929.

"Arsenic Lesions of the Skin," by E. F. Mueller, G. P. Metz, and C. N. Myers. Reprinted from the *Archives of Dermatology and Syphilology,* February, 1927.

XV

WHICH WAY OUT?

FOLLOW YOUR GRANDMOTHER'S INSTINCTS—BACK TO THE ANTE-BRAN, PRE-CRISCO DAYS

Man's instincts are the best guide to his diet—but this is not true for civilized man, for whom this book is written. Primitive man, living beyond the influence of the artificial habits and customs of the civilized part of mankind, has no more need for dietary science or guidance of any kind than the wolf or beaver. When man has normal access to a natural and unprocessed food supply and has not been miseducated by home-economists, or dietitians, or newspaper, magazine, radio, and billboard advertising, he has no more need of advice from Columbia University, or Hearst's *Good Housekeeping*, than does the jaguar, or the python in its native jungle. Unhappily, civilized man's best guide is not *his* instincts, which might lead to enormous overdoses of chocolate éclairs, synthetic raspberry soda, ice cream, hard sauce or hard liquor. Such overdoses of unsuitable foods go with a deficiency or exclusion of lean meat and of such prosaic and commonplace substances, no longer consumed by civilized man unless in limited regions, or for medicinal purposes to correct the damage done by civilized diet practices, as raw fish, raw liver, calves' heads, fish heads, snails, the eggs of wild birds, and tripe, or the stomach lining of animals. The better off economically a person is, the more he has permitted himself to be subjected to the pressures of a business-advertising-dominated social system and the more herd-minded he is, the less value will his food-instincts be to him. The instinct which leads the penniless wayfarer enviously to regard the pastry laden windows of the commercial baker or the typical big-city restaurant is exactly that untrustworthy instinct which stimulates the savage north of the Arctic circle to sit on the wharf and gorge himself to extremes of indigestion on pounds of chocolate candy at one sitting, or to eat the contents of can after can of syrupy peaches and pears, as fast as he can put them away, when a ship from England or America puts into his lonely harbor with white man's food to trade for furs and skins. The instincts that now *should* apply are those of our remote ancestors in the misty past at the dawn of the race, not those of little boys or grown men and women craving jam and sweets, Coca-Cola, and ice cream, in a time when nearly all of the food eaten in many families is of a kind to which man's instincts for food selection and food quantity do not apply.

The instinct that applied to urge primitive man to feed on fresh killed wild fowl or hare, still warm and eaten raw, has little to do with the modern man's behavior in the presence of a roast chicken or turkey which was fed by mass-production methods using the cheapest food giving the fastest gain of weight at the minimum cost per pound, the by-products of cotton manufacture, the flour mill, and the slaughter house; fowl which was raised in a chicken house or pen and deprived of the right to chase insects or other food materials in the prairie or brush, and was fattened to produce the maximum salable weight rather than the best meat; fowl which after

slaughtering was kept a year or more in cold storage so as
to be put on the market at a time that would allow for the
maximum profit to the distributor. There are other things,
some very important ones, wrong with the commercial calf,
hog, chicken, turkey, or duck, judged by what the race *did*
eat, and by what its instinctively wise men know it now
safely can eat, but the points named will suffice to show the
peculiar and delicate nature of the problem of a person
needing to trust instincts in an age when instincts no longer
apply. The wolf whelp or the tiger kitten foraging afield in
its natural environment for the first meals away from its
dam's guiding directions, can always rely upon the fact that
if it captures a live bird, the bird will be eatable and nutritious and wholesome. Transported to civilization the tiger
kitten in search of food might well be poisoned by arsenate
of lead which the bird took into its system by eating grasshoppers or moths or chinch bugs killed with chemical insecticides. The wild bird likewise can be sure that the fruit
which it eats far from the haunts of man, has not been
contaminated with poison sprays or sulphur dioxide, but
man, when he eats an orange or a dried apricot, must concern himself with both metallic poisons like lead and arsenic,
and the unwholesome effects of gaseous poisons like ethylene
or sulphur dioxide.

The native who spears a fish and eats it raw has no need
for the least concern over its wholesomeness unless it be
infected with parasitic worms or other disease condition,
and the native expert fisherman can probably take care of
himself on that score too, by virtue of his superior acuteness
in observation of the condition of health in the animals with
which he is accustomed to deal intimately and skillfully in
his simple and immediate, quite literally hand-to-mouth

economy. But the American who buys a food fish in a Camden fish market buys a very dead fish, almost certainly a badly spoiled fish, quite likely a worm-infested and bacteria-laden fish, about whose condition he has no knowledge or skill of observation whatever, and there is no one in school or even in college to give him the least knowledge or guidance. His professors know the fishes as a problem in ichthyology but not as factors in human nutrition.

The world of modern man is a world too complex for either his mind or his body. It is a world in which business has succeeded in shrewdly organizing the fundamental instincts of the millions for a few other men's profit, where formerly these instincts served for protection of self and race—as they do today for the birds and beasts of the wilds, with which man once ran and hunted.

A world full of healthy, vigorous wild animals and birds and ripe and naturally ripening fruits and vegetables has been changed to a world more characterized by nut bleacheries, orange dye works, egg and meat freezing plants, apricot sulphuring plants, dyed sausage works, chemical hamburger-reclaiming butchers, flour milling and bleaching plants, bread factories, pickle bottlers, and canners and preservers of beef, pork, fowl, fish, fruit, and vegetables.

H. G. Wells, Julian S. Huxley, and G. P. Wells discuss the extensive artificial preparation and processing to which foods are increasingly subjected. They point out that during the canning process there is always a certain amount of chemical alteration of the foodstuffs preserved—vitamins, for example, are destroyed. These authors emphasize the deviation, often touched upon in this book, of many common articles of food from the natural plant and animal tissues upon which our primeval forebears throve, and for which man's digestive equipment is adapted. They point out that sugar itself is not a necessary substance; and that the primitive instinct which led one to sweets such as fruit or honey and other satisfactory foods, is quite inapplicable as a guide to man in the eating of refined sugar and sugar-sweetened foods.

They also show that wheat before it is milled is a richly varied substance, which provides a store of food for the young growing plant just as egg-yolk is a store of food for the young chicken. "Our sub-civilized ancestors mashed up the whole thing to make meal, and as a result they got a nutritious bread. Nowadays milling processes have been perfected until it is possible to sift away everything except the central food-store, and to make bread only from that. [While this refined bread is] much more attractive than wholemeal bread . . . it is poorer both as regards vitamin content and as regards something whose importance has only recently been realized—the amount of rough, indigestible matter that it contains." Note the contrast of the above opinion of the eminent English biologist, Huxley, with the opinion of the equally eminent American biochemist, McCollum, endorser, upon the proper occasions, of white bread for the flour milling interests.

There are a number of things about one's choice of food that can be set down in simple categorical form for the guidance of everyone; there are other points that are of little importance except to those who have some trouble with their general health or digestion. Then there is another whole group of people who need and must have the best of medical advice and care and to whom the proper selection and use of food may be a matter affecting life itself. This latter group should not aim to rely upon the information in this book; they can only be helped by a medical expert who understands their particular problems or allergy or other illness, who can observe their reactions to particular foods, and adjust their diet to their needs as determined by the expert's personal experience and skill. Such persons, however, should religiously avoid advice from two directions, first, the diet cultist, discussed in Chapter VII, and second, the dietitian and professional nutritionist, whose ideas are often almost as absurd, and whose frequent insistence upon the eating of lettuce or spinach, milk or bran, or upon lessened consumption of meat or eggs, has caused many a mild case of undernourishment or malaise to turn into a chronic indigestion or spastic colitis. The diet established by the present-day dietetic and home-economic theories will work, some of the time, for some people, particularly hardy country folk, getting a good deal of exercise, but for millions, especially sedentary workers and city dwellers, and children and old folk, it will spell ultimate illness and undernourishment, and for other millions it has already done so, as any gastro-intestinal physician or surgeon of wide experience can tell you. As to what can be done by the individual about the conditions summed up in this book, it is possible at best for the person of limited income and restricted place of living to do all too little. A few of the things that are possible to people of fair or sizable income are given in the sections which follow.

GENERAL SUGGESTIONS

Eat as much of fresh and fresh killed foods as possible, and as little as you possibly can of canned, bottled, pickled, brined, cold storage and preserved foods of every sort. If you must eat in a restaurant or boarding house, choose one that uses the maximum amount of fresh (not smoked or brined) meat, and eggs, and the maximum proportion of fresh cooked vegetables, especially the non-starchy ones. Avoid so far as possible all sorts of "durable," long-lasting foods, such as hard cakes, crackers, bakers' cakes and cookies, candies, white flour and corn starch and sugar and things made of them; Farina, cream-of-wheat, macaroni, spaghetti, prepared noodles, white rice, and potato chips.

The best safeguard is a varied traditional diet; one of the best dietaries possible is that typified by the French table d'hote dinner; many an American who thought he had chronic digestive troubles has been surprised to find them disappear when he spent two or three weeks on first rate French food, including the dry (not sweet) *vin ordinaire* in a country where wine is wine and not a factory processed soft drink plus added alcohol. The same is true of the food customarily consumed by the comfortable-income classes in Vienna or Prague or in Mexico City. It is chiefly in America or England, perhaps, that one can pay a high price to eat in superior hotels and restaurants, and still fail to achieve a good, well-balanced, attractively cooked, and satisfying dietary.

The general fear of too much protein (or meat and eggs which chiefly contain it) is unfounded. Protein of meats and eggs and fish is very much more satisfactory than that of vegetables like beans; it would require an expert to choose a vegetable, milk, nut and cereal dietary that would assure his getting enough of all the twenty-two amino acids that make up the body proteins. It takes no expert, but only a reasonable dependence upon appetite to get enough and the right protein if lean meats and eggs are freely eaten, and especially if the meats are not limited, as they are by many, to the choice parts of the animal, the so-called muscle meats that make steak and roast beef and roast lamb.

Protein foods are expensive, but they need not unduly swell the food budget except of those who must eat in restaurants. They afford a sense of energy and desire for activity that the starchy and sweet foods do not; those who consume overmuch of the latter will tend to be lazy, lethargic, and slow compared to the meat eater, and the starch eaters will likely in time sufficiently overload their sugar digesting and excreting apparatus that they will run into kidney trouble or possibly digestive sensitivities of various kinds, stomach ulcers, and the intestinal complaints that go with the well-known slow and delayed bowel action of the heavy eater of bread, potatoes and sweets. Exactly such are the difficulties of the enormous populations in the Orient who, on account of extreme poverty and overpopulation, must live almost exclusively on white rice and other foods that are almost entirely starchy in their composition.

There is a general lack of knowledge among nutrition experts of the vitamin and mineral values of meat, no doubt because the subsidies for nutrition research and writing have chiefly come from food processors like the millers and the milk distributors, and because meat packers have been slow to sense, to the extent that dairy and cereal interests have, the advertising value of the names of a few shrewd, highly paid, regularly subsidized nutritionists for their business; but there can be no doubt of the nutritional adequacy of diets high in meat, especially if the choice of meat is varied and includes nearly all parts of the organism, as it does in France and other countries that are famous for fine cookery and good food. The use of stomach walls (tripe), liver, pancreas (sweet breads), brains and other head tissues, kidneys, testicles (sometimes served as "Rocky Mountain oysters," or "lamb fries"), and so on are not merely useful to vary the diet or make it more economical, but they assure its containing needed mineral and vitamin elements.

Anyone who will eat freely of various parts of the animal and fish and fowl from head to gizzard to tripe, and can afford to adopt the general *type* of meal represented by French cookery, which includes soups and broths, many *whole* or complete organisms such as snails, eggs of poultry and of fish, pullets, rabbits, crawfish, shrimps, small fish, and so on, need not worry about his vitamins, nor need he seek dietetic counsel, *especially* from any one who cannot cook as delectable and savory a meal as a first-rate French or Hungarian chef. Good science always presupposes a foundation of good craftsmanship. Take your advice on foods from some one who has qualified by good cookery and a perception of the timeless wisdom distilled into good cookery, and not from men and women who pride themselves on their skill in handling and feeding white rats under highly artificial conditions. (One such "nutrition scientist" fed, under special limited conditions that do not represent the use of canned goods in the home, a number of rats on "74 combinations of 49 different kinds of canned foods" by which he "proved"— to the newspaper reporters who received and passed on the "handout" or news release—that canned foods, without special care in selection of variety or special care to assure large variety, can supply all the dietary requirements of human beings.) When you see rat experiments used as proofs, in the newspaper or in magazines which carry food advertising, of any sort of important question relating to the human dietary; for example, the desirability of sulphuring of dried fruits, you will do well to regard it as proof of the corruptibility of science and scientists by commercial interests, or of the willingness of scientists to emphasize some of their findings and to disregard others. Do not on any account allow such findings to prejudice you in favor of canned goods, ice cream, oranges, dried apricots, or anything else of significant importance in your diet.

For those whose economic situation is such that they must eat large quantities of starchy foods in order to get the needed energy at minimum cost there are some suggestions that will be of value. First, they must get as much exercise, particularly in the open air and especially in sunlight, as possible. When it is not too hot, eat in the sun, if possible. Second, they must obtain as much rest as possible. Longer hours of sleep are necessary on a high starch diet than on a high protein diet, and there is more need for giving full opportunity for digestion to proceed after eating, without sense of strain, hurry, or overwork, than when one eats foods which are more quickly and easily digested, such as meat, fresh fish, and eggs.

The extensive use of wines at every meal, as is practiced in many parts of Europe, is not a bad habit, as it is regarded by the W.C.T.U. and many other moral factors in our American civilization; wine drinking was one of those vital adjustments made by man to an imperfect food and water supply. A diet high in spaghetti, macaroni, and other *pastas* and devoid of the native wine of Italy or France would not be merely indigestible but would be dangerous to health and mental activity.

DETAILED SUGGESTIONS

Never use any canned foods that show the slightest sign of spoilage, such as any off-odor, evidence of gas formation, or cloudiness of the liquid. Swelling or bulging of the ends of the can is a warning of danger. Tin can tops that can be flipped or sprung, represent cans that should be returned to the grocer. In the case of home-canned foods, leaks around the tops or rubber rings, or any sign of internal pressure, as spurting of contents when the jar is opened, call for immediate and thorough destruction, preferably by fire, of the contents. Poisoned canned meat or vegetable or non-acid fruit, such as pumpkin, can be terribly dangerous. The toxin is tasteless and invisible, and is the most deadly poison known to man; so deadly, indeed, that if a bit of food containing it is taken into the mouth and immediately spat out, death may follow. About sixty pounds of the toxin of the *Bacillus botulinus* would be sufficient to destroy the whole human race. Hundreds of cases of botulinus poisoning, commonly called ptomaine poisoning, have occurred, and many occur each year chiefly from home canned meats and vegetables (such as string beans) that do not have an acid reaction and hence, if not heated to a high temperature under pressure (pressure-cooker canning), may provide a fertile culture for the botulinus organism that is present everywhere.

Space does not permit discussing here the special problem of canned foods. Consumers' Research has given much space to this question. Other material will be found in *100,000,000 Guinea Pigs*. Perhaps the most important point is that one must not believe what the canners say about vitamins in their product, because some scientific work of a character similar to that represented in Chapter I of this book was put into the proof, so-called, of the vitamin values of canned foods. A principal reason against the use of canned goods is the disregard by the canners of public opinion with respect to the matter of grading of the kind which will enable the user to avoid paying Grade A prices for the Grade B and C products which predominate in the market. The bulletins of Consumers' Research provide an immense documentation on the disparity between the quality of the canned goods as measured by expert graders and the claims made for them on their labels and in their advertising and by the approval of such agencies as Good Housekeeping Institute.

Dr. C. W. Lieb, writing in *Scribner's* of October, 1934, summed up a good deal of valuable nutritional insight in the following statement from his article, "Design for Eating": "Among the first prerequisites to proper eating is obviously the sanitary and bio-chemical condition of the materials out of which the meal is to be prepared. Artificially ripened fruit, long-stored green vegetables, improperly fertilized plants and fruits, or products of wrongly fed animals, rancid fats, foods containing poisonous spraying chemicals, badly cured or improperly refrigerated meats, poorly canned vegetables, and foods harboring disease-producing flora or fauna, are some of the things we should be on guard against in selecting the raw materials for the home menu." Note his very discerning emphasis (always, so far as I can observe, practically ignored by leading professional writers on nutrition subjects) on the very special and insidious type of adulteration implicit in *"improperly fertilized plants and fruits," "products of wrongly fed animals, foods containing poisonous spraying chemicals, badly cured* [that is, chemically, instead of more naturally] *meats."*

Do not permit your vegetables to be cooked with soda to preserve the color. Do not eat in a restaurant which serves you attractive looking light-green green peas and string beans. Both flavor and vitamins are lost; flavor and vitamin values probably go together, but nutrition experts have not dared to work on so important—and dangerously controversial—a topic, as the relation of flavor to food value.

Green vegetables, such as cabbage, and fruits such as apples, peaches and plums should be cooked as short a time as will make them palatable and digestible. This preserves the vitamins to the maximum, and also the mineral values that are dissolved out and lost when much water is used. A minimum of water should be used and the lid should be left off the pan during the cooking. Beets, for example, should be cooked in very little water, and many fruits and vegetables are better when steamed than when cooked by being immersed in water.

It is a lot of trouble to prepare fresh foods, especially for each meal, but the measure of a good cook is his consistency in doing just this. Cooking large batches, and cooking long before use are both methods that are fatal to pleasurable eating and to best nutritive values. The carrying over of some kinds of foods by canning and preserving and drying is to a certain extent necessary in our climate, but the less these expedients have to be used, the better for health. Ham is no substitute for fresh roast pork, nor canned dried beef for a juicy steak, and let no one tell you the one can ever take the place of the other. Even such foods as whole wheat flour and cracked wheat are entirely different substances, fresh ground, than they are after long storage. Quite likely, certain important vitamin values are lost in the process of exposure to light and air. A hand grinder and some washed wheat makes a breakfast food ready for the pot that has and can have no counterpart in any ready-made product from General Mills or Battle Creek.

People not in the best of health require special care in

selection of diet. Apart from the advice of the physician especially determined by the individual's own problem, one important requirement for those with a not-too-good alimentary tract, especially thin people, is a smooth, non-irritating diet. Foods easily available for such a diet include eggs, lean meat, especially beef and lamb, roasted or broiled, toast (well browned, and not buttered much, nor buttered when hot), butter (in moderation), young carrots, cooked cabbage, sprouts, celery, squash, and turnips, non-fatty fishes and chicken, sweet breads, liver, baked potato, brown rice, asparagus tips (rejecting all the coarse, woody parts), beets, cooked or grilled tomatoes (peeled), and tender string beans. Purées can be used freely, of peas, lentils, beans, lima beans. For dessert, among the most suitable are cooked apples, soft pears or peaches, bananas, well-ripened, and *not* by ethylene gas, baked in their skins, plain cake and not much of it, cheese for those who digest it well, baked soft pears, not the hard, gritty sort, apples, or stewed prunes.

The importance which this writer ascribes to meat in the diet will have been noted by many in their reading of what precedes. There is a great deal of evidence in favor of a large use of meat, especially meat which is fresh from a recently killed animal. If all the edible portions of the animal were eaten, there would of course be no lack of any of the vitamins. Civilized customs have played into the hands of the vitamin fanciers by making it possible for them to popularize artificial additions of vitamins to the food supply, on account of the modern man's, and especially the American's, choosiness as to cuts of meat. Slightly cooked meat is more digestible and otherwise more desirable than meat well done, but pork *must* be well cooked in all its forms on account of the danger of trichina infection, which is always dangerous

and sometimes fatal. Chopped meat is not well digested, as
the minced particles acquire a coating of fat which delays the
action of the digestive juices. Chopped meat is also an
especially good medium for the growth of bacteria, and is
liable to adulteration by water and the addition of chemical
preservatives which become necessary because of the increased likelihood of putrefaction of the cheapened mixture.
Sulphur dioxide is the poisonous and unpleasant preservative which the butcher employs, the same one which is used
for the sulphuring of dried fruit. One should be especially on
one's guard against chopped meats in wayside lunch-rooms
and third-grade or worse restaurants. Smoked meats must
be used with caution, in the first place, because the old-time
smoking process, which was mainly a surface treatment and
left much of the interior of the meat unharmed, is now everywhere abandoned. The present practice is to inject the meat
with creosote, a disinfectant most dangerous to digestion.
The preparation of the so-called smoked meats is now almost
completely chemicalized.

Fish are better eaten only in limited amounts, unless one
has been in close contact with the process by which they
become available. Much fish which passes freely into inter-
state commerce would lack a buyer if it were subject to
inspection by the ultimate consumer on the wharves where it
lies in the sun, sometimes properly iced and protected from
infection and more often not. Fish from polluted streams
are always a hazard, and most streams which pass through
industrialized regions are now grossly polluted. Fish caught
at sea are safer if they come from far out than when they
come from near the mouths of polluted streams or along the
shores of populous regions.

Gassed and dyed oranges are certainly an undesirable

food. That they may be an unwholesome and potentially poisonous food is indicated by some of the information available. It is becoming increasingly difficult to purchase any of the common fruits except apples, that have not been artificially or chemically "ripened." As in the case of butter, eggs, poultry, and fish, the consumer of fruits will do well to buy from local sources and to know something about their handling and their freedom from chemical treatment and from excess spraying with lead, arsenic, and other poisons.

The vogue for frozen foods is not one in which consumers should wish to interest themselves. The object is to increase the extent to which manufacturers and distributors are enabled to collect a somewhat larger part of the producers' and consumers' share of the social income. The sale of frozen fruits containing added sugar is but one of the many ways in which the total content of refined sugar in the diet is being steadily and insidiously increased.

Homemade ice cream has practically disappeared as an article of commerce, and in the process of factory-izing, the differences between good ice cream and bad ice cream have tended to be leveled off to a surprising extent. The state and other legal controls have applied themselves mainly to the question of butterfat content and have paid no attention to how that butterfat content is achieved. Much ice cream, indeed, is hard to distinguish bacteriologically from the water of a much frequented bathing beach. When you make ice cream, as you should if you care for this dish, avoid of course "ice cream powders" and all other ready-made mixtures. The person making ice cream at home should know the freshness, purity, character, and composition of every ingredient she uses.

Malted milk, *Ovaltine* and similar materials are by many

highly overrated as foods. They have no food or other values
that cannot be equally well obtained at far less cost from
commonplace articles of diet.

The so-called acidophilus milk supplies no food elements
not supplied by ordinary milk, and is useful if at all only in
the treatment of abnormal intestinal conditions under a
physician's direction. The radio and other advertising for
acidophilus milk is highly misleading, a characteristic which
seems necessary to make the product salable on a large
scale.

Fruit juices are another item that is highly overrated.
Canned fruit juices now becoming so common that restaurants are getting into the habit of serving them instead of
fresh juice, are by no means the beneficent source of vitamins
that they are commonly advertised to be. The person who is
fussy about his vitamins had better get them direct from
their source and not after they have been subjected to the
ministrations of a commercial canner and a restaurant
keeper. Grape juice and pineapple juice, so much touted as
food drinks, are among the less desirable of the fruit juices.
In older countries the lesson of modifying grape and other
fruit juices by the wine-making process has been well
learned, and a beverage is in this way produced which is
sterile, free from yeasts, free from certain harmful acids,
and which probably has a considerably diminished content of
copper, arsenic and lead compounds, and other insecticide
residues. The tomato juice of the present moment is, of
course, like sauerkraut juice and pineapple juice, just a fad.

Give not the slightest attention to the problem of acidosis
and its cure by the eating of citrus fruits and the drinking
of citrus juices or "mineral water." Recent researches indicate that there is no such thing as acidosis in the sense lately

heavily exploited by leading nutritionists; the fact that
patients suffering from long-continued "acidosis" have not
been helped by the addition of alkalies to the diet supports
this view. The "cure" of acidosis by the excessive intake of
citrus fruits and juices will likely do more harm than good.
The pineapple producers also have made contacts with those
whom the public think are scientists in order to get support
for the acidosis scare, which their advertisements feature. At
the present time the trend of opinion is that an unbalance of
diet in the *alkaline* direction may well occur, in those who
seek to interfere with the natural adjustments of the body's
acid-alkali balance.

It is common to assume that food colors commonly used
in candy, gelatins, etc., are harmless. In many cases they are
not harmless, or they may be at one time and not at another.
The coal tar from which they are made is just not the sort
of ingredient that should be used in the preparation of any
food material. Even home-dyed foods are none too safe unless the process is carried out by the use of beet juice or
something of corresponding simplicity and familiarity.

One of the major atrocities of this age is the disappear-
ance of cheese and the substitution for it on a national scale
of what is called process cheese, made by grinding cheese of
very low quality or any quality that happens to be available
and mixing in chemicals as emulsifiers and sometimes other
substances such as dried milk, milk sugar, or low grade butter. The uniform character and flavor of this product, or as
one should perhaps say, its uniformly low character and
flavor, have accustomed the public to it, and it is now accepted practically without objection by millions who should
know better and who should read the labels on what they
buy.

Poultry, like butter and eggs, should whenever possible be purchased in person from the farm where produced. Much diseased fowl is regularly marketed, government inspection and control being completely lacking. Diseased chickens are of course much easier to avoid when one is familiar with the farm and visits it in person than when one takes pot luck in a public market supplied by a complex and in this commodity notoriously uncontrolled distribution system.

Salad dressings are often undesirable for the same reasons that have been mentioned with respect to vegetable oils. Not only has olive oil commonly been supplanted by corn, peanut, and cottonseed oil, but fresh eggs have been replaced by such products as *Emulsol*, a type of factory-processed eggs now predominantly used. The technique of making salad dressings is to use as little as possible of substantial food materials and as much as possible of starch, cheap edible oil, and water.

Salt should be used in the diet only to the extent necessary. It is very easy to overdo its use, and the tendency to this error will increase as the flavor and vitamin content of the diet tends to be decreased by the refining and milling processes. To the primitive, whose food supply and method of its treatment must be regarded as the norm from which civilized man must not too far diverge, salt was a luxury and a very expensive one. Salt is less needed with a diet high in meat than with vegetables and cereals, because animal tissues contain salt in about the concentration in which it should be present in the human body.

Do not assume that meat extracts and bouillon cubes are in even a slight degree an efficient substitute for meat. Their bacterial count is likely to be high. The salt content added as a filler or make-weight will be sometimes as much as 60 per cent, and the nutritive value of what remains is not to be compared with that of fresh meat.

There are a number of food materials which are especially likely to be adulterated, and some, like Maraschino cherries, are always unfit to eat. Pickles, canned and bottled olives, gelatin and gelatin desserts, canned sardines, fish pastes, and other delicacies especially characteristic of the delicatessen store, represent a few out of many trimmings of the table that are exceptionally likely to contain unwholesome ingredients, and should be treated always as a potential hazard.

Eggs are most digestible when soft boiled, poached, or coddled (which is the method which best insures the whole interior of the egg's being cooked at the same temperature rather than the outside of the white's being overcooked and the yolk's being underdone). Eggs, like butter, are food supplies that one does well to get as directly as possible and from an observed source of supply in the country. It is particularly important that eggs should be from chickens which are not fed artificially and kept confined as in the large poultry farms, but are allowed to run in the fields and eat their necessary ration of grasshoppers, worms, and other country life, and fresh seeds and grass. The mechanized poultry farms produce eggs which are just as undesirable in their way as is the milk from the mechanically managed dairy, where the cows are kept indoors, and fed as mechanically and as routinely as a boiler is stoked with coal or oil.

No one should use factory-made butter who has access to a supply of fresh butter made under country conditions. The factory butter will be far more uniform in flavor, and perhaps in some cases be bacteriologically safer, but it will

be nutritionally less wholesome. Not only should dairy products be purchased from sources where cows live under most
natural and outdoor conditions, and are mechanized and
stall-fed to the minimum extent, but the consumer who cares
about food and its flavor and wholesomeness will do well to
keep a close eye on the dairy farms from which his butter,
milk, and cream come. If he cannot do this, he should at least
not place more confidence in the mass-production and mass-
distribution system than the facts warrant. Many do not
realize that in refusing butter with the distinct flavor of the
farm they are encouraging all sorts of pasteurizing and
renovating processes which make butter bland, to be sure,
but at the same time devoid of the substances which give
natural butter its high nutritive value, as distinguished from
Crisco and oleomargarine.

The enormous consumption of bottled soft drinks, which
runs to 12 billion bottles a year in this country, is one of
the large factors responsible for the excess consumption of
sugar. As in the candy industry, hardly anyone in the
bottled-pop trade uses a wholesome, natural product if there
is something synthetic and highly colored and chemical in
character available. The natural substances have a way of
spoiling which is not shared by the products of "$cience"
that form the main elements of the craft of the soft drink
producers. Proposals by a few radicals that there should be
fruit put into fruit beverages have found little favor in the
trade.

The high concentration of energy in candy, as in sugar,
promotes digestive disturbances; the recent great increase
in diabetes is believed to be related to the increasing consumption of sugar and candy; the unfavorable effect of
candy on the teeth cannot be denied. Especially against the

use of candy is the low state of its manufacturing practice, which is at least as bad as that of the bakery industry discussed in this book. It is even more exceptional for a large scale commercial candy manufacturer to use a natural and assuredly wholesome product than it is for a commercial baker to do so.

Be particularly on guard against the increase at points where it may often pass unnoticed of sugar in common foods. An enormous increase in sugar consumption is brought about by the increase in the use of factory canned fruits and other canned foods as well, which, to be palatable, are often processed with lavish additions of sugar. It is absolutely certain that the present tendency to increase the sugar content of all foods will have disastrous effects upon the national health, since every increase in the calories accounted for in this way implies a corresponding decrease in the calories which are accompanied by indispensable vitamins and minerals. The consumption of the latter is already far too low for safety, as indicated by the growing consumption of cod-liver oil, Vitamin D milk and bread, wheat germ products, and so on, which, once quite properly regarded as medicines, are now becoming conventionally accepted accessories to the debased food supply.

Theoretically, brown sugar would be a valuable substitute for white sugar, since originally it contained mineral substances which to a certain degree mitigated its disadvantageous nature as a concentrated carbohydrate. Unfortunately, brown sugar is now almost the exact equivalent of white sugar except for its color. Molasses, which used to be another one of the sweets that was relatively tolerable, has also been completely eliminated as a wholesome food by the fact that almost invariably it is either sulphured, or is not genuine molasses, even when the label bears that name. One of the forms of sugar which is very common and much used in infant feeding is the well-known, widely advertised corn syrup (really corn-starch syrup). Experiments on animals give good ground for believing that the dextrins that these syrups contain in large amounts are very bad for the alimentary tract—even when a physician prescribes them for use in infant feeding. There can never be doubt that on all possible occasions natural sweets, e.g., fruits, should be substituted for sugared sweets, and canned and preserved fruits, jams and jellies should be kept at a minimum in the diet because of their very high sugar content, which is continually increasing (due, for example, to the use of *Certo*, which greatly increases the sugar content of the finished product).

In the United States, where faddist dietaries are more common than anywhere else in the world and where the food supply has been more interfered with by refining, treating, and milling than anywhere else except England and its colonies, intestinal difficulties of a serious or chronic nature are also more common. This result follows apparently upon an excessive and exaggerated use of bulky or harsh food substances (spinach and bran, for example) engendered by an attempt to overcome the food deficiencies imposed by the millers, refiners, and processors. In the use of meat Americans will do well to rediscover the cheap and common type of cuts which are everywhere used in older cultures and which Americans who have visited Europe find so delicious and so worthy of praise in books and magazine articles. Some of the parts of meat animals discarded in this country but prized by other nationalities are much more valuable nutritionally than the muscle meat and fat that form almost the whole of the American meat dietary. The almost miraculous discoveries with respect to liver as a cure for anemia and the medical value of the stomach lining of animals are examples of the rediscovery by medical men of what primitive man, before medicos, knew without being told. The most important function that home-economists could perform for American nutrition would be to study the diet of the ignorant outlanders and find what use they make of cuts of meat and parts of animals and poultry and fish that here are thrown away. The French stew, bouillabaisse, is an example of such native adaptions to food supply. The Chinese sweetsour stew of spareribs which gets the calcium of the bones into digestively available form in a dietary which would otherwise be especially poor in calcium is another example. Home-economists and nutritionists will resent the suggestion that they should begin their work upon findings of healthy races out of their cultural experience rather than upon a few experiments conducted with animals in neat wire cages. Nevertheless, the most progress in human nutritional research for the future will be made by recourse to the diet of primitive man and of old cultures rather than by a neverending concentration upon the eating habits of rats and guinea pigs, and their reactions to food selections and combinations imposed by a very anthropomorphizing and prejudiced Ph.D. in a nutrition laboratory.

The consumer who eats in a restaurant faces special problems and dangers. The space available in this book did not permit a discussion of the restaurant as a special contributor to the problem of ill health through diet, but at least as much space could be given to that question as to the treatment of baker's products. Even in the better restaurants every sort of expedient is used to cheapen the food at the cost of its digestive safety; numerous unknown and unfamiliar ingredients are added in chopped foods, stews, pie and pastry fillings, salad and frying oils, cakes, ice cream, and many other complex mixtures. Creaming, hashing, and making croquettes of food afford special opportunities for the disguise of spoilage and contamination and other causes of poor condition. In a restaurant, raw foods and salads are an especial hazard on account of the danger of infection with the dysentery bacillus and other organisms, which are far less likely to be a hazard in cooked foods. The epidemic of amoebic dysentery in leading Chicago hotels was a direct result of the handling of raw or cold foods by infected kitchen workers. The dishwashing methods of restaurants and soda fountains are notably unsanitary and very frequently expose the patrons to infection.

The major sin of the restaurant, however, is in its excessive use of canned and processed foods, which decrease the "labor content" of nearly everything served, always the aim of the restaurant keeper. The restaurant also endangers its patrons, in its ever-present tendency to increase the calories, which are a measure of the patron's sense of satisfaction or fullness at the end of his meal, by the overuse of starches and sugar in everything to which they can possibly be added. Both of course are much cheaper and cheaper to handle than meat, eggs and butter. Restaurants tend, as any close observer will note, to skimp on all sorts of fresh, perishable foods such as meat, fish, eggs, and fresh vegetables and so far as possible to substitute lettuce leaves, sliced tomatoes, parsley, and potatoes. Methods of making the platter attractive are often carefully considered means of reducing, by discreet use and arrangement of decoration, the size of the portions of the more costly and more valuable

foods such as meat and eggs. Even dried eggs and canned
frozen eggs are now beginning to appear in restaurant
dishes, from which one may derive an obvious suggestion
as to the desirability of having one's eggs boiled, fried, or
poached rather than scrambled. Gravies as made in a restaurant are especially likely to be synthetic, and digestively
hazardous products.

By all means avoid the use of bran and of bran mixtures,
bran bread, muffins, etc., and of other foods which contain
proportions of roughage not present in any common, normal, non-commercialized foodstuff. To Americans whose digestive tracts have been ruined through excessive use of raw
fruits and vegetables and of bran, breakfast foods and muffins, even the amount of roughage present in whole-wheat
bread may be risky or positively dangerous to intestinal
health until one's digestive system has had a chance to re-
cuperate for some months or even a year or more.

Fat in the diet should be limited, especially for sedentary
workers, and it is far better supplied by butter, cream,
cheese, the fat of meats, (and possibly of eggs) than by the
refined, vitamin-less cooking and salad oils and fats now
almost universally used. Not only are the vegetable fats distinctly at a disadvantage because of their lack of vitamins
and their lower digestibility, but it is known that the relatively indigestible portions of solid fats (e.g. hydrogenated
cottonseed oil, used as a high-priced substitute for lard)
which require a high temperature to melt in the digestive
tract may bring on digestive putrefaction, slow up intestinal
action, and increase the danger, already great, with the
customary American dietary, of poisoning from intestinal
wastes. These high melting-point fats and fried foods, bread,
pastry, and cake made with them will present special dan-

gers, to many, and particularly to persons suffering from arthritis or rheumatic pains, and other conditions of ill health like focal infection.

Fats used and reheated over a long period as they often are in restaurants contain harmful constituents almost certain to make their contribution to digestive troubles. Good animal fats, as above noted, are invariably to be preferred; vegetable shortenings almost without exception are neither as economical nor as safe as those derived from meat and dairy products.

Among the cereal foodstuffs other than bread made of bleached white flour, foods which it may be wise to eat in extreme moderation are farina, *Mello-Wheat*, and *Cream of Wheat;* likewise macaroni, spaghetti and similar products, all of which represent a dietetically very imperfect and unsatisfactory fraction of the wheat germ.

Raw fruits and vegetables are not necessary. They are used in increasing amounts in modern diets, especially at the hands of keepers of tea rooms and directors of college and institutional dining rooms. Many raw fruits and raw fruit juices are very poorly digested. Especially is this true with the now almost universal tendency to eat all sorts of green unripe fruit, from tomatoes to oranges and cantaloupes, that have been "ripened" by artificial methods.

Chocolate and cocoa are food substances of dubious value not only in themselves but because with one exception those that have been tested by Consumers' Research have shown contamination with lead in amounts many times greater than even the lenient official tolerance of the U. S. Department of Agriculture. Dietitians and others have regarded cocoa as a harmless substitute for coffee. Even apart from the probability of its having high lead content cocoa is not a harmless substitute for coffee; it is not nutritionally important; and its high fat content unquestionably retards the digestion of food.

These objections to chocolate and cocoa of course apply to the numerous products in which they are extensively used, particularly chocolated drinks, sodas and sundaes, cakes and candy.

Spices should be used with discretion. They tend to slow down the process of digestion and are known to be a hazard in that they cause stomach irritation, and may after long or excessive use predispose to ulcers or intestinal difficulties. The reality of this hazard has often been tested by those who have accidentally gotten only a moderate overdose of such a spice as pepper or curry, e.g. in eating a tropical dish, and have suffered considerable distress as a result.

Vinegar is objectionable because it so greatly interferes with the natural very mild acidity or alkalinity of foodstuffs. Hence sour and pickled foods should be used only in small or moderate quantities. Furthermore, vinegar is especially likely to be contaminated by insecticidal sprays that have been applied to the apples. Besides, much vinegar is the product of modern factory ingredients and chemical skills rather than of apples and old-time techniques.

Dried fruits represent two dangers: the first from the sulphur dioxide used in their preservation from mold and discoloration and to help increase their moisture content, which permits the sale of water at fruit prices; and the second from the lead and arsenic and other poisonous spray residues. Figs are known to be especially likely to be diseased and infested with worms. Prunes, except for the lead and arsenic hazard, are relatively safe.

When a choice is possible, bread made with yeast instead of baking powder should always be used. No type of baking powder leaves in the food a residue which is entirely harmless.

Proper food well digested is the most important determinant of the condition of the teeth. Time without number it has been proven that damage to teeth can be associated directly and beyond argument with defects in the food supply. Bad diet for even a short period can do irreparable damage to the teeth. Overuse of cereals, including of course bread and cake, has a decalcifying effect which is directly destructive to the tooth structure. Sugar and sweets, starches, and substances predominantly starchy, such as white flour, white rice, and corn starch, are notably undesirable in consideration of their effect upon the teeth. Milk is also bad, in spite of the fact that nutritionists have emphasized its value for the teeth (see *Journal* of the American Dental Association for August, 1935, paper by J. Sim Wallace, physician and dentist, and world renowned specialist in preventive dentistry and dental decay). As is shown on page 1337, the use of candies, especially hard candies such as lollipops, wafers, lozenges, and *Life Savers*, is distinctly disadvantageous to the teeth, as is also the regular use of oranges, lemons, or grapefruit and their juices, which does harm by constantly bathing the teeth in organic acids, so, like cereals, exerting a decalcifying effect on tooth enamel and leading to tooth decay.

The use of liquors, even beer and ale, should for most people be held to strict limits, for two reasons. First, that both beer and ale tend to increase the tendency to over-concentration of energy in the food intake. Beer is high, for example, in sugar. Both are habitually, especially in America, of low quality and unknown ingredients and contaminations, and the high concentration of alcohol in spirituous liquors is a digestive hazard that few can tolerate for a very long time unless they have great native health and vigor and live under conditions where their food supply is notable for its natural and native character. The intake of whiskey which a mountaineer can stand will, by its direct and indirect effects, put a newspaper reporter on a hospital bed much sooner than he is likely to imagine.

By all means eschew added vitamin substances, especially Vitamin D, which is now being incorporated medicinally into all sorts of common foods: canned vegetables, bread, breakfast food, milk, cheese, yeast. Both Vitamin D concentrates and cod-liver oil, which is a principal source of Vitamin D, contain toxic qualities capable of producing heart lesions, as has been noted elsewhere in this book. It is becoming more and more plain that the taking of cod-liver oil and other special Vitamin D substances is the price paid for the privilege of eating a food supply processed and devitaminized in its most essential constituents (bleached-flour white bread and pasteurized milk are two of almost countless examples that might be given), and in order to make life possible in dirty, smoky, and crowded cities where free access of sun- and sky-light to the body and to the food may not occur for months at a time, or at all. The only possible escape lies in seeking a maximum exposure of the body and of as much of the body as possible to light and air, and in working, playing, and eating outdoors in sunshine as far from the smoke, fog, and dust of the city as income permits. Primitive men did not use or require cod-liver oil, but they wore few clothes, worked, played, and often slept in the sun, and ate fresh food mainly from animals whose life and habits were practically a replica of man's own in respect to their continual contact with sun and air and natural fish, animal and vegetable foods.

Suspect and avoid every tendency in civilized living which tends to increase the use of such sophisticated substances as cod-liver oil, viosterol, and Vitamin D bread and milk. We are very near, if we have not passed the limit of man's capacity to adapt himself to city living and foods "civilized" by General Mills, *Good Housekeeping, et al.*

Don't let patent medicine manufacturers, druggists, or salt producers determine your consumption of minerals such as phosphorus, iron, copper, or iodine. These mineral substances will, with the exception of a very few regions, be available in sufficient quantities in natural foods. With the exception of iron, they may do grave harm if taken in excess. Don't worry about vitamins. If you eat the type of diet in which the addition of special vitamin-containing, protective foods as urged by Rose, McCollum, Sherman, and other animal-nutritionists is really necessary to make it safe, you are eating a diet which needs radical revision. It will almost certainly be a diet high in refined (milled) foods, and stale or canned meats, fish, fruits, and vegetables. The more "civilized" and the more sophisticated diets tend to be dangerously low in their content of minerals and vitamins, in direct proportion to the level of luxury which they represent. Dark bread, lentils, liver, heart, tripe, are examples of economical foods that are (relatively) safe to eat in considerable quantities and have disappeared from the diet of well-to-do people. The Vitamins B and D, which are most lacking in the American diet, are exactly the ones which tend to be removed in the refinement of foods. White flour, white corn meal, cornstarch and rice, represent the spoiled end-product of the processing of the cheapest, most commonplace, and for those of small income, the most essential foods.

Don't fall for secret or proprietary foods. Modern advertising *always* emphasizes the advantageous elements which a certain food contains, but fails to mention the other foods which contain the same elements in larger amount and often at far lower cost, and omits reference to the elements which are lacking or to those which may be harmful or of poor digestibility. *No healthy person need eat any secret proprietary foods to have a perfect diet or to maintain normal nutrition; natural, non-secret, staple substances, wisely selected, will always provide what he needs for health, vigor, and efficiency.* Millions of people were healthy and well-fed before *Cocomalt, Paracelsus, Ovaltine,* or *Seavigor* were ever invented or advertised.

As has been frequently pointed out in this book, the avoidance of metallic contaminations in the food supply is impossible for any individual living in civilization and eating foods which pass through our mass-production factories and commercial marketing system. The September 1935 Handbook of Consumers' Research contains a concise and comprehensive summary of the situation with respect to lead and arsenic in the food supply and to tolerances which are half-heartedly applied by the government, and to those which it should apply. For those specially interested in this connection this summary by Consumers' Research will provide an interesting addition to and summing up of the information in Chapter XIV. Other metals are now appearing as menaces in food and beverages. These are principally copper, mercury, selenium, manganese, and fluorin. The foods most likely to contain lead and arsenic, which are the most

pervasive of these metallic poisons, are: cocoa and chocolate, sardines, baking powder, gelatin, the peel or skin of
fruits and vegetables, and, especially, all vegetables such as
broccoli and cauliflower, from which the spray or dust which
has been applied cannot be removed by *any* practicable
method. Even the special parchment papers used for cooking vegetables to retain their mineral substances and prevent
odors may contain lead, and so *add* one very dangerous mineral. The foods affording the greatest likelihood of safety
in respect to lead or arsenic content are: meat (but it is
certain that the natural arsenic content of fish and seafood
is not entirely free of toxic hazard), eggs, dairy products
(although these may contain lead, and commercially distributed milk does often or usually contain an appreciable
amount of lead and sometimes arsenic as well), cereals and
foods made therefrom, root vegetables, and fruits and vegetables of which the skin, hull, or rind is or can be fully removed before eating.

The most important factor in the prevention of colds is
unquestionably the diet, which determines the state of hy-
dration, or water storage, in the tissues of the body. A tendency to colds and increased sensitivity of the skin to
changes of temperature are known to be associated with
an increased retention of fluid in the body tissues. In a series
of experiments by a competent physiologist it was shown
that a diet adequate with respect to protein (e.g. meat,
eggs, fish) and allowing a minimum of carbohydrates
(sugar, starch, bread, cake, potatoes, sweet fruits, etc.) was
most efficacious in the prevention of colds. A diet high in
carbohydrates with restricted protein intake was accompanied by difficulty with colds.

A diet for the prevention of the common cold and preser-

310   Eat, Drink and Be Wary

vation of good health in general will consist, in civilization, as has been indicated at various points in this book, of liberal portions of lean meat, poultry, fish, cheese, eggs, and many other animal products, with the greatest restriction that one's own need for economy permits, of foods rich in carbohydrates such as potatoes, corn, peas, lima beans, bread, cereals, pastry and other starchy foods, and candy, syrup, soft drinks, ice cream, sherbet, and other sweet desserts, many canned fruits, and alcoholic liquors. It is fairly certain that the phenomenal freedom from colds of inhabitants of the arctic regions is traceable to their primitive-man type of diet, low in carbohydrates and composed to the extent of almost a hundred percent of meat protein and vitamin-rich animal fat.

Regardless of the tendencies of one's diet in general, it is certain that to avoid colds and to get well if one has one, one should avoid overloading the stomach with rich foods, gravies, fried foods, richly spiced foods, and desserts, especially rich or sweet ones.

Everyone should work out his own diet so far as his situation and opportunities permit. There are definite differences in the capacity of individuals to handle certain foods such as starch and sugar, and it is one of the sins of the home-economists and nutritionists to assume that particular combinations of white bread and "protective foods" will do for us all. There is as yet nothing corresponding to an exact science on selection or preparation of foods, but it is certain that the more sensible and scientific our selection of diet, the simpler will be the food and its processing and cookery, and the fewer mixed or compounded foods it will contain. Moreover we will be less likely to place em-

phasis upon single food substances or concentrates such as
roughage, or oranges, or the so-called protective foods urged
by Sherman, McCollum, and other leading nutritionists. Almost invariably those foods best adapted to human requirements are those which are to the least degree removed from
their natural condition either in processing or cookery. It
is in the direction of good sense to avoid complication of
food preparation with the mechanics and special material
that characterize, for example, fancy breakfast foods, elaborate salads, sauces, jams, puddings, cakes, and pastries.
Learn to avoid as a habit all foods which furnish calorie
values in concentrated forms, that is, which give high
hunger-satisfaction values in small bulk; or in a form which
is elaborate or complex as to ingredients. In many cases
the stomach and intestines will have as much trouble taking
a complex foodstuff apart for digestion as the cook ex-
pended in putting the ingredients into their complicated
culinary relationships. Learn from the untutored savage,
whose cookery was as simple and direct as the nature of his
food supply permitted, because he ate as he played, loved,
and slept, by instinct and by his native culture, without
benefit of home economics, guinea pigs, white rats, or Good
Housekeeping Institute.

INDEX